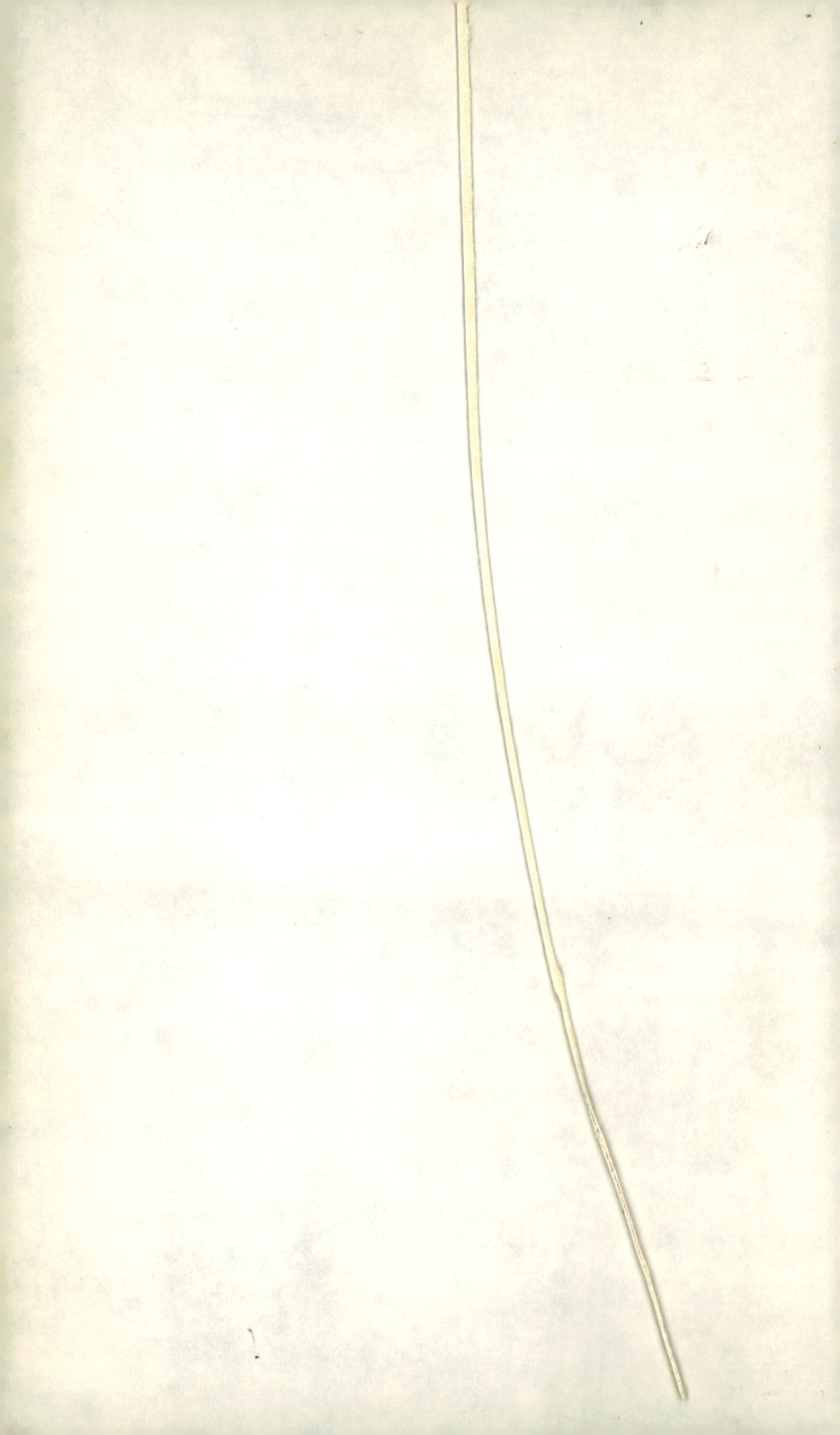

A GUIDE TO THE EARLY CHRISTIAN AND BYZANTINE ANTIQUITIES

IN THE DEPARTMENT OF

BRITISH AND MEDIAEVAL ANTIQUITIES

PLATE I. LEAF OF A BYZANTINE IVORY DIPTYCH: THE ARCHANGEL MICHAEL.
(*See* p. 169.)

BRITISH MUSEUM

A GUIDE TO THE EARLY CHRISTIAN AND BYZANTINE ANTIQUITIES

IN THE DEPARTMENT OF BRITISH AND MEDIAEVAL ANTIQUITIES

SECOND EDITION

WITH FIFTEEN PLATES, A SKETCH MAP, AND
A HUNDRED AND FIVE ILLUSTRATIONS

PRINTED BY ORDER OF THE TRUSTEES

1921

PRINTED IN ENGLAND
AT THE OXFORD UNIVERSITY PRESS
BY FREDERICK HALL

PREFACE

THE edition printed in 1903 having been exhausted, the opportunity has been taken of rewriting the old Guide, a course rendered necessary by the great extension of Early Christian and Byzantine studies in recent years; only a few parts, including the pages on the Greek Church and on Heresies originally contributed by Mr. Henry Jenner, have been reprinted as they stood. The principle adopted in the First Edition of devoting a great part of the space to introductory matter has, however, been retained, even though within the narrow limits imposed nothing beyond a bare abstract can be attempted. There is a real need for a short general survey, since few among the visitors to the Museum have leisure or opportunity to master the extensive literature of the subject, and without some framework of knowledge the collections lose much of their meaning. Early Christianity penetrated countries differing widely in culture and tradition, and various peoples helped in the formation of its art. It is an advantage to know what the main influences were, and how they are to be distinguished, before passing to an examination of the objects in the Cases.

In a great historical Museum, where collections are arranged according to civilizations and periods, a detached series representing a cosmopolitan religion introduces a cross-division. The same object may have importance both from the Christian point of view and from that of a pagan culture related to Christianity; or it may be more suitably placed among antiquities illustrating the arts of a particular country, for example, those of Egypt. All the objects in the Museum which interest the student of Christian Art cannot therefore be brought together in the Christian Room. But the inconvenience caused by their separation is in great measure compensated by the gain of seeing them in relation to contemporary works of other kinds from the same area; the variety of the sources contributing to the formation of Christian Art is thus more fully realized.

The Guide has been written by Mr. O. M. Dalton, Deputy Keeper of the Department, who was also responsible for the first edition.

The Trustees are indebted to the Delegates of the Clarendon Press for permission to use the blocks for Figures 15, 54, 71, 88, and 100, and to the Society of Antiquaries of London for Figures 33 and 34.

C. H. READ.

CONTENTS

	PAGE
List of Plates	viii
List of Illustrations in the Text	ix

INTRODUCTION

PART I. GENERAL SURVEY.

I. GEOGRAPHICAL DISTRIBUTION	2
II. INFLUENCES AFFECTING THE DEVELOPMENT OF CHRISTIAN ART	13
III. HISTORICAL SURVEY	24
a. From the beginning of the Christian Era to the accession of Constantine as sole Emperor, A.D. 323	24
b. From the sole rule of Constantine to the Arab Conquests	27
c. From the Arab Conquests to the End of Iconoclasm in A.D. 842	40
d. From the End of Iconoclasm to the Fourth Crusade of A.D. 1204	48
e. From the Fourth Crusade to the capture of Constantinople by the Turks (A.D. 1204–1453)	53

PART II. SPECIAL SECTIONS.

I. EARLY CHRISTIANITY IN BRITAIN	56
II. THE CATACOMBS, AND EARLY CHRISTIAN ICONOGRAPHY	69
III. CHURCHES AND THEIR CONTENTS	91
VI. THE ARTS	116

APPENDIX.

I. COPTS AND ABYSSINIANS	152
II. THE GREEK CHURCH	157
III. HERESIES, AND GNOSTICISM	159
IV. IMPORTANT DATES	163

DESCRIPTION OF CASES, ETC.

WALL-CASES	167
TABLE-CASES	183
OBJECTS IN OTHER PARTS OF THE MUSEUM	187
INDEX	189

LIST OF PLATES

I. Leaf of an ivory diptych: the Archangel Michael   *Frontispiece*

	PAGE
II. Ivory panels from a casket. Early fifth century (see p. 88) .	20
III. Ivory panel: the Baptism. Sixth century	34
IV. Ivory boxes of the sixth century: Daniel in the den of lions, and the martyrdom of St. Menas (see pp. 169, 170) .	56
V. Byzantine ivory panel: the death of Jacob (see p. 169) .	64
VI. Silver bridal casket of Projecta (see p. 174)	80
VII. Top of the silver bridal casket of Projecta: portraits of the bride and bridegroom	94
VIII. Byzantine silver treasure from Lampsacus. Sixth century (see p. 175)	106
IX. Byzantine silver treasure from Cyprus (see p. 173) . .	116
X. Gilded glasses: Our Lord and a family group . . .	130
XI. Gilded glasses: Daniel and the dragon; a gladiator (see p. 186)	142
XII. Bronze ewer and basin from Spain (see p. 172) . . .	146
XIII. Cedar panels from Cairo: the Annunciation, Baptism, and Ascension (see pp. 171, 172)	154
XIV. Russian enamelled brass cross (see p. 167)	168
XV. Gilt bronze cross from Abyssinia (see p. 181) . . .	180

LIST OF ILLUSTRATIONS

(The numbers in brackets refer to the *Catalogue of Early Christian Antiquities*, printed by order of the Trustees, 1901.)

	PAGE
1. Medallion of Valens, showing the *labarum*	2
2. Inscribed stone from a Christian grave, Semirechensk	5
3. Tombstone from Spain: fourth century (No. 934)	8
4. Tombstone from Carthage (No. 937)	9
5. Limestone sculpture from Wadi Sarga: sixth century	11
6. Stand for water-bottles, Wadi Sarga: sixth century	12
7. Coptic sculpture from Medinet el-Fayûm (No. 944)	14
8. Coptic sculpture from Medinet el-Fayûm (No. 945)	16
9. Bronze lamp on pricket-stand (No. 496)	18
10. Bronze lamp: fifth century (No. 502)	19
11. Bronze lamp with sacred monogram (No. 501)	21
12. Bronze patera (No. 534)	22
13. Silver bowl with cover, Carthage Treasure	25
14. Bronze steelyard-weight: the Emperor Phocas (No. 485)	26
15. Lead flask with the Incredulity of Thomas: sixth century	28
16. Bronze reliquary cross: twelfth century (No. 559)	30
17. Painted pottery fragments, Wadi Sarga: sixth century	31
18. Top of the silver casket of Projecta (No. 304)	33
19. Section of dome-shaped silver casket, Esquiline Treasure (No. 305)	35
20. Pottery lamp with Jonah and the whale (No. 718)	37
21. Pottery lamp from Syria (No. 835)	38
22. Pottery vase with two faces, Wadi Sarga: sixth century	39
23. Design on an earthenware plate from Egypt (No. 926)	41
24. Pottery lamp, probably from Egypt (No. 822)	44
25. Fragments of painted pottery from Wadi Sarga: sixth century	46
26. Fragments of painted pottery from Wadi Sarga: sixth century	49
27. Gilt bronze plaque: St. Theodore: eleventh century (No. 544)	50
28. Gold ring engraved with a fish (No. 48)	52
29. Gold ring engraved with the sacred monogram (No. 28)	52
30. Gold ring with openwork inscription (No. 49)	54
31. Gold marriage-ring: fifth century (No. 207)	54
32. Gold marriage-ring with designs in niello (No. 129)	55
33, 34. Two rings with sacred monogram from Fifehead Neville, Dorsetshire: fourth century	58

LIST OF ILLUSTRATIONS

	PAGE
35. Early Christian basilica, Silchester; Church of Celtic plan at Escomb, Durham	61
36. Plan of seventh-century basilica at Reculver	62
37. Plan of seventh-century basilican church at Wing	63
38. Stamps with sacred monogram on Roman pewter from the Thames	64
39. Silver chalice of the time of Alfred, from Trewhiddle, Cornwall	67
40. *Loculi* in the Roman catacombs (after Perret)	70
41. A chamber in the Roman catacombs (after De Rossi)	71
42. Inscription from the Roman Catacombs (after Marucchi)	73
43. Front of a marble sarcophagus from France (after Le Blant)	74
44. Engraved gem: fish, crook, and palm-branch (No. 35)	77
45. Engraved gem: a ship (No. 40)	77
46. Engraved gem: anchor, fish, and dove (No. 3)	77
47. Engraved gem: anchor, doves, palm-branch, fish (No. 39)	77
48. Engraved gem: the Good Shepherd (No. 2)	77
48a. Engraved gem: dove with olive-branch on fish; sacred monogram (No. 6)	78
49. Harts drinking from fountain, mosaic from Carthage: sixth century	79
50. Reconstructed *labarum* (after J Wilpert, *Die römischen Mosaiken und Malereien* etc. 1916)	80
51. Pottery flask: St. Menas between camels (No. 860)	82
52. Front of a marble sarcophagus of the fourth century: Cupid and Psyché (British Museum)	83
53. Gilt bronze brooch with sacred monogram: fourth century (No. 256)	85
54. Ivory panel from a book-cover with the Nativity and Adoration: sixth century	87
55. Engraved gem: the Crucifixion (No. 43)	88
56. Exterior of Old St. Peter's, Rome	92
57. Interior of Old St. Peter's, Rome	93
58. Exterior of the Church of the Apostles, Salonika (after Texier and Pullan)	96
59. Church of Amba Derho, Abyssinia (after J. B. Bent)	98
60. Plan of a basilica	101
61. Plan of a Coptic church (after A. J. Butler)	101
62. Bronze hanging disk for lamps (*polycandelon*): sixth century (No. 529)	103
63. Altar with ciborium, Italian: ninth century (after Rohault de Fleury)	104
64. Glass vessel from Amiens, perhaps a chalice: fifth century (No. 658)	107
65. Silver chalice, probably from Syria: sixth century	108
66. Liturgical diptych from Egypt: seventh century	109
67. Coptic *flabellum* (after Butler)	112

LIST OF ILLUSTRATIONS

	PAGE
68. Silver censer from Cyprus: sixth century (No. 399)	113
69. Coptic Eucharistic bread and spoon (after Butler)	115
70. Wall painting from Wadi Sarga: the Three Children of Babylon: sixth century	118
71. Head-piece from an eleventh-century MS. in the British Museum (Harley 5785)	120
72. Coptic decorative sculpture: sixth century	123
73. Coptic decorative sculpture from Wadi Sarga: sixth century	124
74. Coptic limestone capital: sixth century	125
75. Marble slab carved on both sides from Miafarqin: 10th–13th century	126
76. Silver spoon with cross in niello, Carthage Treasure: early fifth century (No. 364)	128
77. Stamps on the base of the silver censer, fig. 68	129
77a. Monogram and inscription on spoon of the sixth century, Lampsacus Treasure (No. 390)	129
78. Pierced gold disk; centre-piece from an ornament of chains to cover breast and back: Egypt: sixth century	132
79. Byzantine gold pectoral cross with inscription in niello (Galatians vi. 14) (No. 285)	133
80. Byzantine gold pectoral cross (No. 287)	133
81. Gold bracelet: sixth century (No. 279)	135
82. Gold ring: fifth century (No. 190)	135
83. Gold ring: sixth century (No. 189)	135
84. Silver ring worn as an amulet (No. 142)	135
85. Engraved gem: the Good Shepherd; Jonah: fourth century (No. 25)	136
86. Onyx cameo: the Annunciation: eighth century (No. 104)	136
87. Heliotrope cameo: bust of our Lord (No. 106)	136
88. Byzantine coins: Justin II (A. D. 565–578) to Basil II (A. D. 975–1025)	138
89. Byzantine bronze pound-weight, with two saints inlaid in silver: sixth century (No. 483)	139
90. Byzantine bronze money-weight: sixth century (No. 453)	140
91. Glass disk with scriptural subjects, found at Cologne (No. 628)	141
92. Bottle of blown glass, with cross: fifth century	143
93. Glass cameo medallion with bust of our Lord: eleventh century (No. 686)	144
94. Glass cameo medallion with St. Theodore: c. twelfth century (No. 693)	144
95. Glass pendant with the Good Shepherd: fourth century (No. 697)	144
96. Byzantine gold ring with cruciform monogram: fourteenth century (No. 171)	146
97. Byzantine bronze ring with inscription: c. eleventh century (No. 139)	146

LIST OF ILLUSTRATIONS

	PAGE
98. Gold and nielloed reliquary: 10th-11th century (No. 284)	146
99. Tapestry medallion on a tunic from a Coptic cemetery (No. 951)	148
100. Silk textile with mounted figures from Egypt: sixth century	151
101. Coptic tombstone: 7th-8th century (No. 942)	153
102. Abyssinian priest at entrance to Holy of Holies (after J. T. Bent)	155
103. Abyssinian silver chalice	156
104. Abyssinian priest's rattle	156
105. Abraxas, from a Gnostic gem	162

SKETCH MAP

Showing places of importance in the earlier history of Christianity 3

INTRODUCTION

PART I. GENERAL SURVEY

No general introduction to the study of Early Christian and Byzantine antiquities can avoid serious difficulties in classification and arrangement. There is little agreement as to the point where the Early Christian period should end or the Byzantine begin: the very meaning to be assigned to the latter term raises a fresh problem. Moreover both terms, as commonly used, tend to exclude the earlier Middle Ages in the West which succeeded the fall of the Roman Empire. Yet between the fifth and ninth centuries, to carry the limit no lower, Early Christian influences, largely from the East, continuously penetrated the barbaric West, and the period commonly known as the Dark Ages cannot be understood unless the penetration is borne in mind. That period, too often treated as a gulf between late classical and mediaeval times, should rather be regarded as a bridge connecting the two.

For the present Guide, which retains its old title, the term Early Christian will be extended to the ninth century, an extreme limit, but one allowing us better to appreciate the continuity of artistic influence. In the East, this century witnessed the beginning of an age to which the name Byzantine may be more correctly applied than to any preceding it, an age of which the influence upon the western world was more closely associated with Constantinople than before. In the West it marked the growth of the Frankish Empire under Charles the Great which inaugurated a new era, though at the time of its birth it was still deriving motives of its art from earlier Christian sources; it marked the final decay of the earlier Christian art of Rome. With the ninth century, therefore, a division may conveniently be made, and the later part of the survey will in general be confined to the East. But in its account of conditions in the Byzantine Empire it will continue to lay stress on the close connexion between East and West down to the rise of Gothic art and the dawn of the Italian Renaissance.

Some such comprehensive treatment as that above indicated is almost a necessity at a time when exploration has in a quarter of a century doubled our knowledge of the Christian East, forcing us to realize, as never before, that throughout the first millennium of our era the physical unity of the Eurasian continent found clear reflection in its art. It is no longer possible without distortion of the facts to cut short the Early Christian period at the fifth century, or to divide the field of mediaeval studies at the Adriatic. The area of distribution is no less continuous than the sequence of the centuries; and though both in space and time convenience may demand the drawing of artificial boundaries, it is essential that the underlying unity should first be recognized.

I. GEOGRAPHICAL DISTRIBUTION.

The study of Christian antiquities must begin with some knowledge of the manner in which Christianity spread through the ancient world. (*See* Sketch Map.)

The East.

Palestine. The Christians of Jewish birth, who formed the earliest community, soon yielded in importance to men of other races, because the Jews as a body remained loyal to their old religion. When the new town of Aelia Capitolina was built by Hadrian at Jerusalem, its Christian population was composed of Gentiles, at first Greeks, then in an increasing degree Syrians and Armenians. In all Palestine Christianity was from a very early date the religion of immigrant peoples. The first Christian communities were chiefly found in Greek cities, of which the principal was Caesarea, scattered through a country where the spoken tongue was for the most part Aramaïc (Syrian), though Greek was the liturgical language. Taking the country as a whole, it may be said that down to the first quarter of the fourth century Christians were numerous, but not in the majority. In the northern part of the Roman Province of Arabia, down the east side of Palestine and south of the

FIG. 1.—Medallion of Valens, showing the *labarum*.

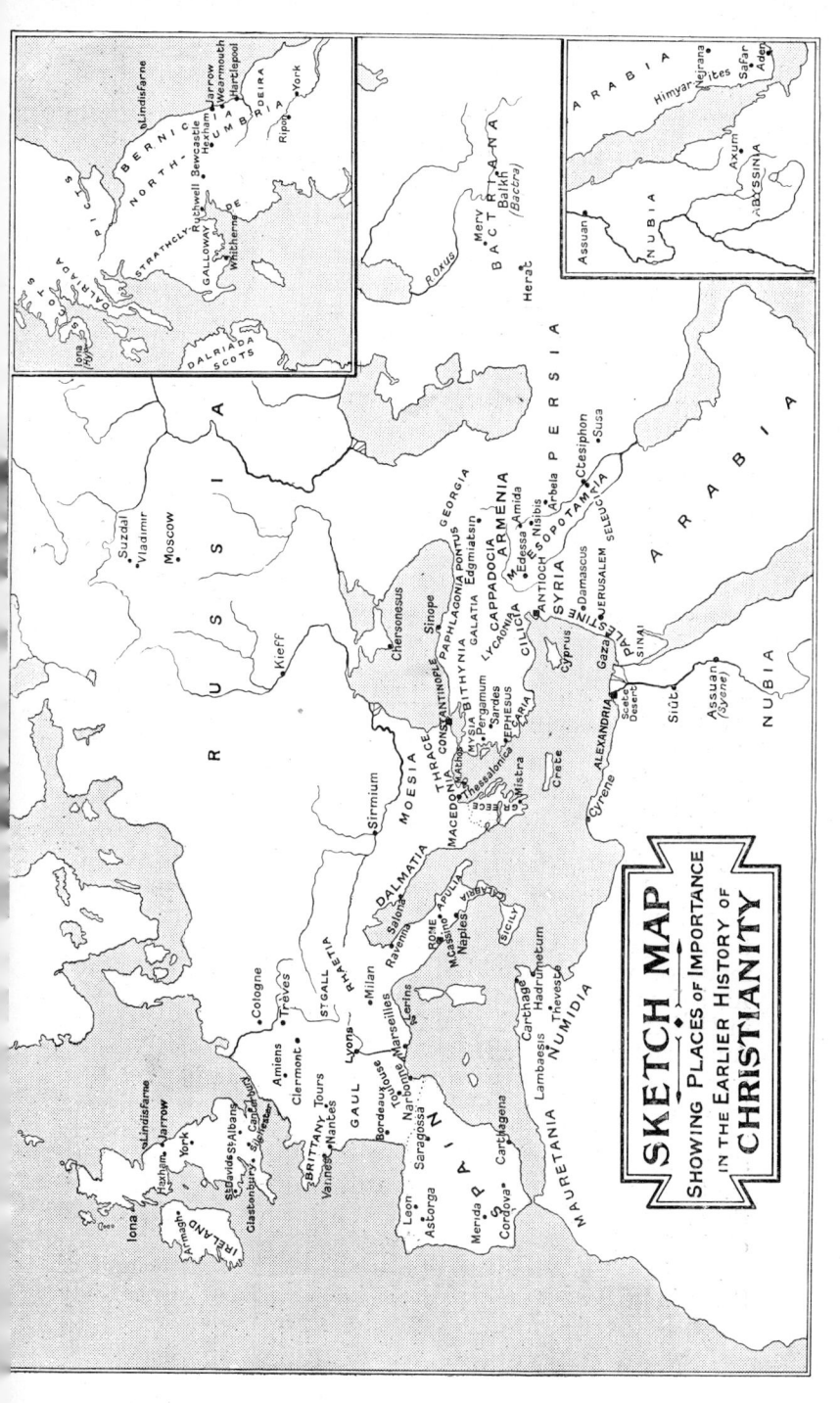

Dead Sea, we hear of Christians at Bostra (Bosra) in the third century, and at Gerasa (Jerash) before A.D. 325.

Syria and Mesopotamia. Here Antioch on the Orontes was the great centre of Greek Christianity from apostolic times (Acts xi), the influence of the city extending to the north-west over Cilicia and Cappadocia in Asia Minor, to the East, through Syria proper, into regions beyond the Roman frontiers—North Mesopotamia, Persia, Armenia, and even Georgia. In Syria, Aramaïc was spoken throughout the country districts, and the Syrian spirit penetrated the life and modes of thought even in the Greek-speaking cities. Thus Greek and Syrian Christianity were closely united from the very first, and the subsequent influence of Syria in the Holy Land is easily understood. In Northern Mesopotamia, Edessa (Urfa) in Osrhoëne formed, from the close of the second century, a great missionary centre. In A.D. 202 the prince Abgar IX was baptized, and in the third century the city was the stronghold of Syrian national Christianity; here the Scriptures were translated into Aramaïc, which now took its place beside Greek in Christian literature; here, and at Nisibis not far away, were schools of theology, the influence of which in later times extended far through the Christian world. To the missionary zeal of Edessa is due the fact that before the fourth century the new religion was established farther north at Amida (Diyarbekr), north-east at Arbela, in Adiabene beyond the Tigris, and south-east at Seleucia opposite the Persian capital Ctesiphon on the lower course of that river.

Armenia and Georgia. The Christianization of Armenia seems to have begun in the south-west, from the Cappadocian side; it was therefore due in the first instance to Greek rather than to Syrian Christianity, and the immediate source of influence was Caesarea in Cappadocia; later, Edessa and Antioch made their own contributions. There were Christians in Melitene, south of Lesser Armenia, in the time of Marcus Aurelius (A.D. 161–80). In Greater Armenia Trdat III (Tiridates) was converted by Gregory 'the Illuminator', who had been trained at Caesarea; under this king Christianity was adopted as the State religion about A.D. 300, that it might help to affirm Armenian nationality against the Zoroastrian Persians on the south-east. Beyond the Caucasus Georgia followed the example of Armenia, and was Christianized in the course of the fourth century.

Persia. The Christian communities of Adiabene and of Seleucia in the Persian sphere of influence have been already noticed; there is evidence that the new faith entered the former region in the second century. Persia itself was penetrated at the same early period, and both under Parthians and Sassanians Christianity enjoyed a large measure of tolerance. It was often the policy of the Sassanian dynasty to support a religion in disfavour with the Roman Empire; after

FIG. 2.—Stone inscribed with cross and inscription in a form of Syriac; it served as a tombstone for a Nestorian Christian. From the neighbourhood of Lake Issik Kul, Province of Semirechensk: 13th-14th century (p. 168).

the Peace of the Church, there was more persecution, but even then it was not continuous. In the earlier fifth century, the heretical views of Nestorius, the Syrian patriarch of Constantinople (p. 159), were suppressed within the Byzantine Empire, but were allowed to obtain a firm foothold in Persia, where in the sixth century the Nestorian Church grew rapidly and began to extend its influence farther to the east. It established itself in Margiana and Bactria south of the Oxus, with its chief seats at Merv, Balkh (Bactra), and, further south, at Herat. Its missionaries crossed the Oxus, and pushed into inner Asia (cf. fig. 2).

China. In the seventh century they had entered China through Turkestan, and their progress in that country is attested by the well-known monument at Si-gnan-fu, with its Syriac and Chinese inscriptions dating from A.D. 781. The success of Christianity in China during the eighth century had been such that it seemed almost likely to become an official religion. It failed, however, to maintain itself against the growing opposition of Buddhism and Confucianism, and by the tenth century it was almost extinct.

India. In this country, the north-western parts of which seem to have been reached by a much earlier mission associated with the name of St. Thomas, the Nestorians established themselves in the south, in Malabar and in Ceylon. The name of India seems, however, to have been applied by early writers to the country of the Himyarites in Arabia Felix (Yemen) which Pantaenus of Alexandria is said to have visited as a missionary towards the close of the second century.

Egypt and Abyssinia. The introduction of Christianity into Egypt is traditionally connected with a mission of St. Mark at Alexandria. Little is known, however, of the progress made in the first two hundred years, but it must have been rapid, for by the close of the second century a flourishing Church was established in the city with Greek schools of Christian learning. In the third century the converted population was very numerous, and about the middle of it the Scriptures may have already been translated into Coptic. The country became renowned for the number of anchorites living in solitude in remote parts, especially the Skētē Desert, the Natron Valley, and the Thebaid, and in the fourth century paganism almost entirely disappeared. In Cyrenaica, to the west, there was by the third century a Church in relations with that of Egypt; the conversion of Nubia south of Assuan began in the sixth century at the instance of Theodora, Empress of Justinian. Abyssinia, with its capital Axum, had been Christianized from Alexandria in the fourth century. The Abyssinian Church has always maintained relations with the Coptic (cf. p. 154).

Asia Minor was the most Christian territory in the Empire, for here the new religion had no stubborn or highly-organized pagan rival to overcome. The Greek cities of the coastal region were quickly converted, and the extent to which Christianity spread in the west of Anatolia is shown by the letters written to Trajan by Pliny when proconsul of Bithynia in the second half of the second century. Christianity everywhere fused with the later Hellenism; Ephesus as a Christian centre ranks only second to Antioch, and 'Asia' (Lydia, Mysia, Phrygia, and Caria) contained other towns, Sardis, Pergamon, and Smyrna, with large Christian populations. Lucian says that Pontus was full of Christians in his time. In rural parts of the peninsula like Cappadocia, the fusion with local pagan belief proved no less easy, and Christians were very numerous in the middle of the third century. The organization of Asia Minor in bishoprics was already complete before the conversion of Constantine. We have seen that in the south-east the Christians of Cilicia and Cappadocia looked rather to Antioch, which was accessible to them, than to Ephesus which was far away.

Eastern Europe.

Moesia and Thrace. The west coast of the Black Sea was early Christianized from Bithynia on the opposite shore; in Thrace and eastern Moesia, corresponding to the modern Bulgaria with the territory to the south of it, there were many Churches before the fourth century, maintaining relations with Asia Minor. But in most parts of the Balkan peninsula Christian communities were small and scattered before the foundation of Constantinople. In Macedonia and Greece, Corinth and Thessalonica (Salonika) had flourishing communities in the first and second centuries. In Athens, the city of philosophy, progress was slow, and neither Greece proper nor Macedonia developed a national Christianity, like that of Syria and Egypt. In Central and Western Moesia and Pannonia, the regions south of the Danube extending as far as the Eastern Alps, there were Christian communities in the third century, and bishops from these parts were present at the first (Nicene) Council in A.D. 325. The Serbs and the Bulgarians crossed the Danube into this part of the old Roman Empire in the seventh century. The former were converted in the first half of the ninth century, the latter in the reign of Boris I in A.D. 864. In Dalmatia, Salona (Spalato) may have been a Christian centre as early as the second century.

The Greek cities in the *Tauric Chersonese* in the south of

Russia appear to have contained Christians before the fourth century: two bishops present at the Council of Nicaea in A.D. 325 are thought to have come from here. The Goths in the interior were already in part converted before A.D. 325; they had been brought into contact with the new faith through

FIG. 3.—Tombstone from Spain: fourth century. (No. 934.)

their raids into Asia Minor, especially into Cappadocia. In A.D. 258 they brought back from such a raid Cappadocian Christians who in their exile maintained communication with their native country, and spread the Gospel among their new masters. The Mesopotamian monk Audius, banished to these parts shortly before the time of Ulfilas, devoted himself to missionary work among the Goths. Ulfilas, 'the apostle of the Goths', was himself a Cappadocian carried off in a raid; his labours among the tribe date from the first half of the fourth century. The above relations between the Goths and Christians from Cappadocia and Mesopotamia may have their importance for the spread of artistic forms from East to West (pp. 32, 33). Slav Russia, which had become acquainted with

Fig. 4.—Tombstone from Carthage: 4th-5th century. (No. 937.)

Christianity in the later tenth century, was formally converted at its close after the baptism of Vladimir at Kieff.

The West.

Italy. Rome was from the first the metropolis of all the centre and south. But during the first three centuries the eastern part of the North Italian plain looked rather to Pannonia and Macedonia; Sirmium and Thessalonica were at this time as accessible to them as Rome, which gradually extended its influence through the north after A.D. 325. This early outlook towards the Greek Christianity of Salonika should be borne in mind in connexion with subsequent artistic relationships. In the western part of the northern plain the expansion of Christianity appears to have been slower than in the eastern. The first Christians in Rome were largely Greeks, and Greek remained the language of the Roman Church until the end of the second century; the list of Bishops of Rome down to this time contains few Latin names. This does not imply an exclusive Hellenization during the whole period; for though it was not until almost the middle of the third century that the Church became predominantly Latin, there must have been services for the Roman-born quite a hundred years earlier. The community at Rome grew rapidly both in numbers and wealth, and the city was divided by Fabian into quarters or *regiones* about A.D. 250. The whole of Central and Southern Italy, with the island of Sicily, acknowledged the Bishop of Rome as metropolitan. In Naples we may infer from the existence of the catacombs that there must have been an important Christian community as early as the second century.

Gaul. The traditional relations of the south coast with the Eastern Mediterranean ensured the establishment of Christianity at an early date in the south of the country (Gallia Narbonensis and Lugdunensis), where trade was carried on not only by Greeks and Syrians, but by orientals of various races and countries. There were Christians in the Rhone valley by the middle of the second century, and Lyons had a bishopric before A.D. 177; the first small community at Lyons was almost certainly Greek, though Irenaeus mentions the conversion of Celts; Greek probably remained the language of cultivated people in Gaul as late as the third century. Further to the north there were communities, but perhaps not bishoprics, before Constantine at Clermont, Grenoble, Limoges, Chartres, Angers, Orleans, Senlis, Metz, Soissons, Toul, Troyes, and other places. In Belgic Gaul and Germania the early Church was not numerically important. At Trèves a bishopric was founded in the second half of the third century, but there seems to have been only a single small place of worship until after the Peace of the Church; the city continued to be mainly pagan through the fourth century. It may be inferred from Irenaeus that there were bishoprics both at Cologne and Mayence about A.D. 185. At Cologne, too, there was only one small church; and probably in the greater part of Gaul, except the south-east and the Rhone valley, the position of Christianity resembled that of Trèves. In the fifth century, with the increase, in the south, of monasteries maintaining regular relations with the East, the progress of conversion became more rapid; the Gallo-Roman population was not Christianized as a whole until about A.D. 450, but the number of bishoprics was considerable before that time. In Aquitaine, the Visigoths were Arian Christians (p. 159); and when in the first decade of the sixth century the Franks displaced them, they too were Christians, but Catholics, Clovis having been baptized by St. Remy in A.D. 496.

In Armorica (Brittany), there appears to be some evidence of Christianity at Nantes in the time of Diocletian (A.D. 284-304), and of a small community in the same place about

FIG. 5.—Limestone sculpture from Wadi Sarga: sixth century.

the middle of the fourth century. But little is known until after the missions originated by St. Martin (A.D. 372–97). In the early fifth century the bishopric of Nantes was definitely organized, and another bishopric established at Rennes. A third bishopric, that of Vannes, was founded about A.D. 465, at the time of the Saxon devastations which put an end to the Gallo-Roman Church in this part of Gaul. For the peaceful invasion of Celtic Britons which followed, see p. 57.

Britain and Ireland. (See p. 56.)

Spain, a country Romanized in pagan times, had Christians certainly in the second century, and possibly much earlier. In Cyprian's time (middle of the third century) there were communities in Leon, Astorga, Merida, and Saragossa. The holding of a Synod at Elvira, about A.D. 300, shows by the list of attending bishops that Christianity must have been established in all parts of the country. The invading Visigoths, in Spain as in Gaul, were Arians.

Germany and Scandinavia. East of the Rhine, i.e. beyond the Roman Germania, conversion began in the first half of the eighth century under St. Boniface, a native of England; Prussia did not become Christian until a later time, and Lithuania not until the fourteenth century. Christianity entered the Scandinavian countries in the tenth century.

Africa (North-West) must be reckoned with Europe rather

Fig. 6.—Limestone stand for water bottles, from Wadi Sarga : sixth century.

than with its own continent, since in imperial times its maritime relations with Rome were much closer than those by land with Libya and Egypt; it was the great Roman granary, and was almost regarded as a part of Italy. From the end of the second to the end of the third century there was in this part of the world, especially in its eastern half (Numidia and the Proconsular Province, corresponding to the modern Tunisia), an expansion of Christianity comparable to that witnessed in Asia Minor. The writings of Tertullian (fl. *c.* A.D. 190–214) allow us to assume a large community at Carthage. In its earliest years the African Church seems to have been Greek, but there were soon many Punic converts; the indigenous Berber element seems to have been hardly touched. The greatest increase in Carthage and 'Africa' generally was between A.D. 211 and A.D. 249, by which time Latin culture predominated. The imposing ruins of cities in the present French colony remain to show what the prosperity was in Roman times, and the Christian monuments are both numerous and important, including the remarkable catacombs of Susa or Hadrumetum (Sousse). In A.D. 429-39 Africa was conquered by the Vandals, who were Arians, and subjected the Catholic inhabitants to indignity and persecution. In A.D. 535 it was recovered for Justinian by Belisarius, and remained a Byzantine province until the close of the seventh century, when it was subdued by the Mohammedans.

It can hardly be doubted that the centre of gravity during the early Christian centuries was in the East rather than in the West. The numerical majority must have lain with the converts east of the Mediterranean, while Asiatic Greeks, Syrians, and other orientals formed the nucleus of early western communities at Rome, Carthage, and the cities in the south of Gaul. The superiority of the East in most elements of higher culture, in letters, science, and art, was even greater; the possession of the single city of Alexandria was itself almost enough to ensure this result, and Alexandria by no means stood alone.

II. Influences affecting the Development of Christian Art.

It is impossible in the present place to examine at any length the reasons why Christianity expanded in a few centuries over so wide an area of the ancient world. It must suffice to say that it responded better than its competitors to the general religious needs of the age in which it was born, and that the conditions surrounding it at its birth were favourable for success.

The expedition of Alexander the Great ($d.$ B.C. 323) into Asia had not only removed political frontiers, but had broken down spiritual boundaries. The Greeks, dissatisfied with their traditional gods, looked round them in these new fields for fresh foundations of belief; they sought to bring together the elements of some universal system which should embrace not single peoples only, but all mankind. After Alexander the conception of such a system may have been formed by many speculative minds; but the renewed dissensions of the world clouded the vision, and it was not until the rise of the Roman Empire that it again seemed to be brought near. In the long interval many regions of ethical and religious thought had been explored. The destiny of the individual soul had moved into the foreground; men's minds had become familiar with the ideas of redemption, atonement, union with God, immortality in a world beyond the present; the universal kingdom seemed more possible after the rise of the Roman Empire with its

Fig. 7.—Coptic sculpture from Medinet el-Fayûm: 5th-6th century. (No. 944.)

vast extent and its equality for all men before one law. But the religion which should be at once personal and world-wide had not yet been found when Christianity appeared in a central position, under the political supremacy of Rome and the intellectual supremacy of Greece. Polytheism, its most obvious enemy, was already weakened, and destined to fall by its own decay. The only serious rivals of the new faith were those which attempted to solve religious problems in ways more similar to its own. These were Persian Mithraism, the mystical philosophic system known as Neo-Platonism, and Manichaeanism, another Persian doctrine which assumed the character of a Christian heresy. Of these three beliefs Mithraism was the least to be feared. It found little intellectual support, because it never made progress in the Greek lands; it was a faith carried westward chiefly by traders and by the oriental soldiers in the Roman army. Although, by its ultimate association with emperor-worship, it obtained a head-quarters at Rome, it was for the most part confined to the stations in the provinces and along the frontiers occupied by the Roman garrisons. It has been described as chiefly a religion of the circumference, rather than of the centre, and was therefore inevitably defeated by one which controlled the great seats of intellectual life. Both Neo-Platonism and Manichaeanism were more formidable rivals. The first had disengaged from grosser elements the spirit of Greek religion, and blended it with philosophy, suffusing it with mystic thought, and colouring it with the emotional feeling of the East; the second, founded by Mani, a Persian subject, born in A.D. 215, blended a Babylonian dualism with Christian, Zoroastrian (Mazdeist), and Buddhist elements. Both sought to satisfy the spiritual yearnings which troubled the world, and both won a great measure of success. But each had a source of weakness which Christianity was able to avoid. Neo-Platonism was without a Founder able to quicken the imagination of mankind at large; Manichaeanism, like Mithraism, failed in its appeal to the Greeks, perhaps because of its austerities, and found bitter enemies among orthodox Zoroastrians. It was thus too much thrown back upon the East and too bitterly opposed at home to succeed in universal conquest; it became known as an oriental heresy, and its more permanent successes were confined to the eastern half of the world.

Christianity, on the other hand, obtained the support of Greek thought. It rapidly fused with Hellenism, and, finding in the intellectual and widespread Greek population an unsurpassed agent of expansion, established itself in the Greek cities from Seleucia on the Tigris to Lyons on the Rhone. It obtained in like manner the support of the Syrians, now the most highly endowed among the Semitic peoples, and, like the Greeks, traders and travellers; their theological zeal, their missionary activity, based upon the schools of Edessa and radiating through the middle and the farther East, with the commanding influence which they exerted over monastic thought, made them invaluable allies. Finally, it secured much tolerance in Persia, partly for the political reason mentioned above, but also, it can hardly be doubted, because it was able to share fundamental ideas in Persian religious thought, such as the eternal dualism of good and evil. Christianity thus brought itself into intellectual and moral accord with the three principal peoples in Hither Asia. But the relation was

Fig. 8.—Coptic sculpture from Medinet el-Fayûm: 5th-6th century (No 945.)

not intellectual and moral alone; it could not fail to be artistic also. These three peoples all had peculiar creative gifts; between them they shared the most active artistic traditions of the age, and their association with the new faith insensibly led to results of high significance for the future of art. It will be well briefly to estimate their several contributions in this field, beginning with the Greeks.

The Mediterranean Greeks after the time of Alexander had reacted aesthetically no less than intellectually to their environment. In philosophical and religious speculation they had compressed into single systems, by a process commonly described as syncretism, elements widely different in origin. They followed the same course in their art. At the beginning of the Christian era this was already far removed in spirit and manner from the Hellenic art of the great periods, and transfused by oriental influences coming to it from the whole area conquered by the Macedonian arms. Three centuries of such transfusion had left it still predominantly a figure art, but profoundly changed in spirit. Though much of the old idealism survived in centres where the Greek population was purest, as in parts of Asia Minor, elsewhere, perhaps through contact with Syrian and Mesopotamian Semites, it had been largely replaced by naturalism. The tendency to naturalism was encouraged by Alexandrian science, which disposed men to scientific rather than to emotional vision; it was from Alexandria that attempts to develop true perspective were probably derived.

Another change from the old Hellenic point of view was caused by the growth of the symbolism prevalent in the East. This was directly encouraged during the first three centuries by the repressive action of the Roman government, which prevented the open representation of Christian subjects. The paintings of the Catacombs, the manifestation of Early Christian art long most familiar to us, illustrate the symbolic tendency in its Hellenistic dress, though in certain elements not introducing the human figure analogies to oriental symbolic art have been conjectured (p. 24). A third change concerned the treatment of ornament. In earlier Greek times this had been regarded as subsidiary: it now began to claim independent and substantive existence; and spaces which the old Greeks would only have allotted to figure subjects were encroached upon by continuous and diffused patterns. The new ornament invaded sculpture, which in course of time gave it an ever readier welcome, adopting the oriental methods which bring out the design no longer by modelling in relief, but by light and shadow in a single plane, and create an impression like that produced by patterned textiles (p. 127).

Late-Hellenistic art remained primarily a figure art, and by this its place in the service of Christianity was assured. But it had become rather an art of cleverness than of sincere feeling; it thus creates an impression of superficiality. By itself it was not qualified to satisfy the needs of the new religion, which called for more sincerity and force than it was able to give. But the Greek powers of composition and arrangement made it indispensable when the time came for the introduction of a historical art after the Peace of the Church. The first historical themes and cycles were the work of Hellenistic Greeks, and, in Italy, of Romans who had assimilated their style.

The contribution of Syria to the formation of Christian art would appear to have been determined by the Semitic genius, though Syrian feeling was shared by the Copts of Upper Egypt and by non-Semitic inhabitants of inner Asia Minor whose outlook on the visible world was in many ways the same.

At the beginning of the Christian era the Syrians were the chief representatives of old Assyrian and Babylonian traditions. Their art was naturalistic and, like that of the Greeks, concerned with the human figure. But its spirit was different from the Greek. The Semitic mind, as has often been remarked, is content with limitation if it can attain certainty; it is dogmatic, and free from hesitation in matters of belief. It is not reticent in rendering either fact or emotion; as in questions of fact it expects the bare truth, so in feeling it will not stop short of the full expression. In a story or sequence of facts it demands all the facts, the homely or the repellent no less

FIG. 9.—Bronze lamp on pricket-stand, probably from Egypt. (No. 496.)

than the attractive. Therefore its naturalism was strict and realistic, disregarding all the Greek ideas of measure and restraint. It sought to represent the object, not as a symbol, but as an end in itself, a clearly defined unity possessing individual form; at the same time, though it had an intellectual basis, it was not experimental or scientific. Semitic art was coloured by the psychological qualities of the race. But it was also affected by memories of the ancient civilization in the valleys of the Tigris and the Euphrates, which had encouraged the growth of an advanced monarchic system. Under the great ancient

Fig. 10.—Bronze lamp: fifth century. (No. 502.)

monarchies the ideas of the king as a divine being, and of the god as a being with monarchical attributes, were deeply implanted in the minds of the people. With the coming of Christianity these ideas intervened to modify the conception of Christ; the carpenter's son of Nazareth, the Good Shepherd of early symbolism, became the Lord of All and the Supreme Judge. The hierarchic feeling which permeated Semitic life reacted upon art in less general ways. Thus the most important personage in a scene had not only to have the central position, but a stature exceeding that of secondary persons. The result is that in Christian art where the Semitic influence is powerful we have what has been called 'inverted perspective': the figures in the foreground are smaller than the central figures, and this not for aesthetic, still less for scientific reasons, but on purely psychological grounds. In ornament the Syrians and Copts seem to have developed rather than invented, transmitting decorative methods and designs received from farther to the east. Here Syrian art was already contaminated by Persian influence. Like Hellenistic art, it absorbed a wealth of formal motives, based upon animal and vegetable forms, which apparently came into it in large part from the North Iranian area: such was the formal vine-scroll enclosing beasts and birds in its convolutions, so common in mosaics, stone sculpture, ivory carvings, and other works of art. It also adopted Persian technical processes. Though representing the culture which gave the world the great Assyrian reliefs, it seems to have lost interest in figure sculpture; Syria, outside Antioch, has yielded no important figure reliefs and no statues. It adopted the Iranian principle of substituting for modelled forms delineation by contrasted light and shade, or juxtaposed flat colour (p. 117). The effects of these changes were far-reaching when in the fifth century the two representational arts, the Hellenistic and the Syrian, were brought into alliance under the domination of the Church.

The foregoing paragraphs have suggested that the Persian share in the formation of Christian graphic art mainly consisted in the gift of new decorative principles and designs. In contradistinction to the Greek and the Syrian, Persian art was primarily an art of ornament. The figure-art of southern Persia which we describe as Sassanian was not indigenous, but influenced in a representational direction from Mesopotamian and Hellenistic sources; its chief aim was the glorification of great kings after the Assyrian and Babylonian precedent. The art really characteristic of the country flourished rather in the northern regions, where Persia came into contact with the steppes and their nomadic peoples. This art might indeed include forms of men, animals, or plants. But it did not use them, like that of the Syrians and pagan Greeks, as ends in themselves, but as pure symbols, or, more frequently, as constituent parts of a decorative design; they were conventionalized and fitted into geometrical pattern. The Iranian artist did not see things in depth, but in flatness; as above noted, he did not carve in high relief; in painting he avoided modelling in tone, and applied flat colours side by side without gradation. Since his field of vision had but two dimensions and

PLATE II. IVORY PANELS FROM A CASKET. EARLY FIFTH CENTURY.
(*See* p. 88.)

THE DEVELOPMENT OF CHRISTIAN ART 21

all was perceived in one plane, he had no concern with true perspective; his flat figures were all brought to the front, and if by exception degrees of difference in distance had to be supposed, were placed in zones one above the other, those regarded as farthest being at the top. He disliked centralized design, preferring the diffusion of continuous pattern, outlined by opposition of colour or of light and shade. These characteristics already appear in the art of the steppes which for convenience we describe as Scythic, centuries before the beginning of the Christian Era, and belong also to peoples of Turco-Mongolian stock; this fact, and their absence from the pre-Christian art of Egypt, leads us to suspect that they originally came into Coptic,

FIG. 11.—Bronze lamp with sacred monogram. (No. 501.)

as earlier into Syrian art, from the north. They explain the probable Persian descent of the wall-decoration by brilliant colour in various materials which lent the interiors of early Christian churches so much splendour. In construction Persia may have played a great part in the development of Christian architecture through that of Armenia.

It will be pointed out below that from the toleration of Christianity under Constantine the Church demanded a historical and dogmatic art, and that in the fifth century the increasing power of Church and State, and their mutual understanding, subjected art to a new ecclesiastical and imperial control (p. 27). At the end of these paragraphs dealing with the three main artistic influences which determined the course of Christian art, it may be well to point out in anticipation the natural result of this joint religious and secular demand for sacred representation.

A compromise became necessary between the two representa-

Fig. 12.—Bronze patera. (No. 534.)

tional arts, the Hellenistic and the Syrian, which were those most immediately affected. Though for many reasons, above all for its fervour and sincerity, the Semitic element commended itself more than the Greek to a church now largely influenced by Semitic monasticism, it was impossible for more than one reason to build up a new art on this foundation alone. Hellenistic co-operation was essential. The Greeks were better organized, having more trained artists and more technical knowledge. They had the habit of composition and a genius for ordered arrangement; they were thus more capable of designing individual scenes and logically ordering them in cycles. They had a whole repertory of conventional attitudes and gestures useful for the presentation of ordinary action. They were without rival in the field of sculpture. Moreover they enjoyed the support of the Court, and of the more highly educated classes which were indoctrinated from youth up with classical tradition. Hellenistic art therefore possessed both practical qualities and prestige; it was indispensable at a period of rapid change. The comparatively untrained Syrian monastic artist had to copy it and borrow its details; at a time of pressure the Church had to give it welcome. But though Hellenistic talent might contribute largely to form, Semitic zeal, with all monasticism behind it, was bound to provide the spirit, and, except in predominantly Greek environments such as those of Alexandria and other great Greek cities or at the Byzantine Court, the spirit bent the form to its will. Persia, whether or not she had shared in the earlier Christian symbolism (p. 24), lost influence in an art now openly representational and didactic; her ornament did not serve the ecclesiastical need of the moment. The Syrian-Greek alliance in the representation of the fifth century was an event of high importance for Christian sacred art, which it was destined to influence both in East and West for centuries, and in the East alone down to modern times.

The above account of the chief influences contributing to the development of Christian art may now be followed by an outline history of Christian art within the limits suggested in the opening paragraphs. Although precise classification is necessarily artificial, and, if regarded as anything more, is likely to mislead, it yet provides useful stages at which the mind may rest on a long road. The following divisions are here adopted as a matter of convenience:

- a. From the beginning of our era to the accession of Constantine as sole Emperor, A.D. 323.
- b. From A.D. 323 to the Arab Conquests in the first half of the seventh century.
- c. From the Arab Conquests to the end of Iconoclasm in A.D. 842.

d. From A.D. 842 to the taking of Constantinople by the
      Crusaders in A.D. 1204.
   e. From A.D. 1204 to the capture of Constantinople by the
      Turks in A.D. 1453.

III. HISTORICAL SURVEY.

a. From the beginning of the Christian Era to A.D. 323.

During these three centuries the official attitude of the Empire towards the new faith checked the growth of Christian art within its borders. Christian expression, as we find it in the Catacombs (p. 69), is symbolic in a Hellenistic style which differs from contemporary pagan art in little but the nature of the subjects. At the very end of the period, when sculpture was employed to decorate Christian sarcophagi, the same treatment continued; in the Greek cities and in Italy there is no Christian style to be distinguished from the pagan. The minor arts followed the same lines; here too the Christian character is betrayed only by the subject or by inscriptions. As church-building was not permitted to develop, Christian architecture made no real beginning.

We have seen above (p. 4) that long before the Peace of the Church there were Christian communities in Persian territory beyond the Roman frontiers; that Edessa, now under Roman, now under Persian control, established Christianity in the early third century during a period of Persian supremacy; and that the Armenian royal house made it the state religion about A.D. 300, some years before it was tolerated in Rome. In view of these facts, and of statements made in early chronicles, it seems possible that places of worship may have been built in Persia before the time of Constantine, in which case some of them may well have been constructed and decorated in the Persian rather than the Hellenistic manner; no actual remains of this time have, however, been preserved, and the erection of such buildings is not yet proved. We may perhaps assume that, if they existed, they were decorated with animal and floral ornament, or even with hunting and fishing scenes, a Persian style of decoration; a correspondence on this subject between St. Nilus and the founder of a new church shows that the kind of motives described above had been usual in the churches of Asia Minor during the fourth century. If, as has been conjectured, these animal and floral designs had a symbolic meaning for Zoroastrianism, capable of adaptation to Christian belief, there may have been in the East a second Early-Christian symbolic art of Persian derivation, contemporary with the Hellenistic symbolism of the Roman and Alexandrian catacombs, and possibly even finding some reflection in the West. In the first three centuries there was no powerfully organized Church interested in the control of art. Local influences were allowed free play; and the simultaneous existence of different ornamental or even symbolic styles in different parts of the Christian world is not in itself improbable. If the Greeks introduced, as they did, Orpheus and Psyché as Christian symbolic figures, Persian Christians might equally well have adapted the formal symbolism of the country in

Fig. 13.—Silver bowl from the Carthage Treasure: 4th–5th century. (No. 361.)

which they lived, and the usage might have spread westward after the manner of other Persian fashions. Future exploration and research may throw more light on these possibilities.

It is interesting to note that while within the Christian area both in East and West art still remained symbolic, and the time of Syrian influence had not yet come, the Semitic spirit was already affecting the late-Hellenistic sculpture of Gandhara on the North-West frontier of India. This art of the second and third centuries, devoted to the service of Buddhism, is narrative and episodic in a manner which suggests inspiration from Antioch, where the Syrian spirit informed a Hellenistic art. In Gandhara the forms are Greek, and venerated persons are directly represented, whereas in Buddhist art before the time of Graeco-Syrian influence they were suggested only by symbols.

This period witnessed the beginning of monasticism, which had long existed in India, especially among Buddhists. It began with the withdrawal of devout persons into remote or desert places to live the life of hermits. Anchorites, whose

Fig. 14.—Bronze steelyard-weight: perhaps bust of the Emperor Phocas (A.D. 602–610). (No. 485.)

numbers rapidly increased from the middle of the third century, constructed their cells within reach of each other; they came to form groups, especially in Egypt, where at the end of this period St. Pachomius established the first organized community at Tabennisi near Denderah (c. A.D. 315–320), thus beginning a movement destined to a swift expansion in many countries, and ultimately exerting a profound effect on the direction of Christian art.

Resuming what has been said above, we find the first period marked by two main characteristics: the symbolic character of its art, and the absence of any central controlling power giving that art a definite direction. The symbolic art which prevailed in Italy and the Mediterranean cities was late-Hellenistic in style, owing its first inspiration, as far as painting was concerned, chiefly to Alexandria, but in sculpture to the cities of Asia Minor and to Antioch; in Rome native artists adopted the style and learned to give it their own expression, so that a Roman Christian art came into being. Beyond the eastern boundaries of the Empire Christians living in Persian territory may well have used an Iranian form of decoration, itself perhaps symbolic, but differing in character from that which we see in the Catacombs. The absence of a central ecclesiastical authority controlling the development of art was favourable to originality and to local initiative.

b. *From* A.D. 323 *to the Arab Conquests in the first half of the seventh century.*

The toleration of Christianity in the Roman Empire essentially changed the position of Christian art. A liberated Church desired to proclaim its triumph and openly to set forth its sacred story; symbolism therefore gave place to a historic sacred art. In the eastern provinces oriental influence progressively increased at the expense of the Hellenistic; partly because the eastern Christians were numerically powerful and more fervent than the Greek, partly because the new historic and dogmatic phase upon which art now entered was attractive to the Semitic mind. At first, however, for the reasons mentioned above (p. 23), the Greeks remained indispensable; in the earlier sarcophagi, manuscripts, and ivory carvings their influence is still paramount. We have seen that they had the technical experience and the practice; they had numbers of trained painters and sculptors; the oriental had much to learn from them in such matters as composition of figure subjects or the arrangement of themes in cycles. The Hellenistic artist now turned from the symbolism with which he had hitherto been occupied to scriptural history and the illustration of dogmatic truths. In painting Alexandria seems for a while to have kept her supremacy; the designs of a scroll in the Vatican Library, illustrating the life of Joshua, and reproducing an original MS. of the fourth century, show how purely Hellenistic much of the first Christian historical art must have remained. But a Greek predominance so exclusive as this could not be more than temporary. The Syrians were naturally predisposed to history and dogma; they had at the same time the dramatic sense. Borrowing or adapting from the Greeks all that they needed, they were soon able to give characteristic expression to their religious feeling. The fifth and sixth centuries marked the steady growth of their importance in religious art, and a relative decrease of Greek influence. In Italy the encroachment of the East was less rapid. There is a continuity between the sacred art of the catacombs and that of the Roman churches; a classical style persists in the nave mosaics of St. Maria Maggiore (A. D. 352–366), and may be presumed in the case of other early picture-cycles now lost, for instance in that of the great Lateran basilica. In the fifth century oriental influence is apparent in details, largely as a result of relations with Ravenna; but the tradition of Roman Christian art survived the troubles of the time, lasting to the close of Theodoric's reign: the apse mosaics of SS. Cosmas and Damian were produced in the year of that king's death (A. D. 526).

Fig. 15.—Lead flask with the Incredulity of Thomas. Obtained in Egypt, but probably made in Palestine: sixth century.

Thus although in the East Roman Empire the Hellenistic element was far from being suppressed, and in secular art probably survived almost unimpaired at Constantinople, the whole of this time is marked by a continuous process of orientalization. A new Christian religious style now appeared, in which the eastern factor became preponderant and impressed its character upon the whole. It was an art fond of episode and realistic in detail, yet in representations of sacred persons insisting upon the ancient connexion between God and king, between the royal attributes and the divine. This suggestion of the supernatural took its place beside the homely and outspoken realism in which grace was disregarded and emotion rendered without restraint. Both were Semitic, not Hellenic tendencies; and in proportion as they gained ground the Greek element was forced into the background. But, like the Hellenistic expression which it now largely superseded, this orientalizing art was itself contaminated by Persian influences. It took over Iranian formal ornament to frame or set off its figures. Though it accepted Greek help in ordering its subjects, and, within the subjects, adopted attitudes and gestures which were commonplaces of Hellenistic practice, it was averse from the general intellectual trend of late-Greek art, and more especially from its effort after true perspective and its modelling of round form. Modelling was reduced to a minimum or abandoned for the use of flat colours side by side; where perspective would naturally be required, and its own inverted perspective (see above, p. 20) did not suffice, it adopted the Asiatic method of zones one above the other, the uppermost zone representing the most distant part of the field of vision. Thus East-Christian art now became a compromise between two representational systems, the Semitic and the Greek, each of which, but especially the former, was modified in certain directions by Persian influence. The new art was didactic in tendency; from the ecclesiastical point of view it was indeed a form of pictorial instruction, regarded by the Fathers as an important adjunct to oral teaching. Mural paintings and mosaics, now in great demand, illuminations, ivory carvings, were all designed to teach and edify by means of carefully chosen scriptural or other subjects; the arrangement was often rigidly systematic, as when the parallelism between the Old and New Testaments was observed. Early mosaics of the churches at Rome and Ravenna illustrate the didactic tendency of the time; minor works of art preserved to us suggest that the same influences obtained in the Holy Land, and the description left by Choricius of Gaza of the cycles painted in the sixth century on the walls of the Church of St. Sergius in that city introduces us to an art of which the spirit is wholly different from that of the Catacombs.

The progress of this new sacred art from the fifth century onwards was furthered by various causes. The monasteries, which rapidly increased with the substitution of common life under a rule for that of anchorites, gradually became important centres of art and craftsmanship. But monastic learning was now largely directed from the schools of Edessa and Nisibis in Northern Mesopotamia, which were under Syrian control. Monastic art and iconography tended in consequence to receive a Syrian impress, diffused by the close relations between the religious houses in different countries throughout the Christian world. Through such relations the Syrian spirit obtained the ascendancy in the monasteries of the Holy Land; it probably determined the nature of mosaics and paintings in the memorial churches to which pilgrims now flocked from all parts. It thus attained a world-wide repute, for the designs of the mosaics and frescoes of the Holy Places were copied in such portable mementoes as the *ampullae* or flasks (fig. 15) which the pilgrims took home from their travels. Moreover, since the illumination of books was chiefly the work of monks, and since these books were carried from place to place to be copied in distant countries, the orientalizing monastic style largely inspired the earliest representational art of mediaeval Europe. The interesting early Gospels in the Library of Corpus Christi College, Cambridge, are held to be such a copy, the model being perhaps a sixth-century illuminated Gospel book like those preserved at Rossano and in Florence (p. 122). In addition to monks and pilgrims, traders must have borne their share in the distribution of minor works of art through the West. Here again the agency was in great part Syrian, for though that adjective is used by early writers in a wide sense and includes other orientals, the Syrians were among the most active of the commercial peoples settled in the Mediterranean ports. Ivory carvings of which the subjects are closely related to those in illuminated MSS. may have passed through traders' hands with other portable objects in the ordinary way of commerce. Gregory of Tours, writing in the sixth century, relates that the

Fig. 16.—Bronze reliquary cross: twelfth century. (No. 559.)

Merovingian king Chilperic was furnished with works of art by a merchant of oriental birth, a fact which suggests traffic in such things with the East. Another influence which tended to the diffusion of art was the exchange of gifts between Constantinople and the Teutonic courts of Europe. Sometimes we infer that the foreign gift provoked the emulation of the barbaric prince. Thus Gregory tells us that Chilperic, who had received presents from the Byzantine court, commanded his goldsmiths to make a large gold dish to show what Frankish skll could do.

It has been already stated that the Copts, though of a different race, shared the general aesthetic standpoint of the Syrians. They took their share also in the dissemination of the new art. But the Syrians, through the eminence of their theological schools and their monastic influence, seem to have assumed a certain control of sacred art; Coptic figure art seems to have had a less extensive influence.

Fig. 17.—Painted pottery fragments from Wadi Sarga: sixth century.

The Copts were relatively more important as masters of decorative design, which they developed in a remarkable manner after the fourth century. Like Syria, and probably through Syria, Christian Egypt derived ornamental methods and motives from Iranian sources; the technical methods of decorative sculpture (p. 127), for the execution of which the Copts used with admirable effect the limestone of the Nile Valley, seem to belong to the art of Asia rather than to that of ancient Egypt; while the number of motives common to Syria and Coptic Egypt favours the hypothesis of Asiatic rather than Egyptian origin, especially when we remember that both the formal floral scroll and the vine as ornament are believed to have come into Egypt from Asia. Coptic industrial art has enjoyed an advantage over that of Syria and Persia through the fact that Egypt has long been available for systematic excavation, and the exceptionally dry soil has preserved even articles of a perishable nature. Christian antiquities from Egypt have necessarily outnumbered those from other places not so favourably conditioned; and, not unnaturally, the art of other parts of the Christian East, less in the public eye, has been in some measure overlooked. A universal initiative has thus been assigned to the Copts without sufficient evidence. But this said, it may at once be admitted that the native Egyptians excelled in all manner of decorative practice; that they developed designs with individuality; and that in their tapestries they may perhaps claim invention. Their production was very large, and in the wide distribution, by commercial and other means, of objects made in various parts of the Christian East, Coptic products are conspicuous. If the silver plate of Antioch has been discovered in the remote East-Russian province of Perm (p. 129), bronze vessels of Coptic types have been found in Anglo-Saxon cemeteries. And, in the actual transmission of eastern ornamental designs to Gaul and the West, Coptic Egypt may have borne a greater share than Syria.

But if Iranian ornament penetrated the West chiefly through the intermediary of Christian Copts and Syrians, it had enjoyed other and more direct means of access. The style of gold jewellery set with a mosaic of table garnets or coloured pastes in cells (*orfévrerie cloisonnée*, inlaid jewellery) certainly followed the Goths from the Black Sea region, and it is unlikely to have been the only artistic importation brought by this tribe from the Persian borders, and transmitted to other Teutonic peoples. The wide diffusion and popularity of this jewellery and of other ornamental methods of like origin enable us better to understand the reception accorded to the new sacred art in all countries from the South of Russia to the West of England. The ground had been already prepared, the artistic sense of the Goth, the Lombard, the Burgundian, the Frank, and the Saxon already trained in a Persian school.

When these tribes received Christian works of art with ornament designed on the same principles as their own, they gave it a ready welcome. The Irish Celts themselves, who were without a figure art, at once perceived the interest of new decorative designs; this is why the introduction of Christianity into Ireland was followed by an influx of eastern ornamental motives, which naturally took their place beside the spirals and trumpet-patterns of native art.

Fig. 18.—Top of the silver casket of Projecta. (No. 304.)

It is possible that the migrating peoples brought with them from the East forms of more direct importance to Christianity than these. It has been maintained that a knowledge of stone building may also have come in with the Goths; this people in early days had raided Cappadocia, carrying off prisoners (p. 8), and was converted to Christianity before the great westerly movement began. In North Syria and Cappadocia, and possibly in Armenia, the period between the fourth

and seventh centuries was fertile in architectural experiment;
and certain very early churches still standing in France and
Spain, on soil once Visigothic, are generally admitted to show
oriental features. It is argued that they are early successors
of churches erected by eastern builders entering the West in the
train of the Goths. The question, which is controversial, is
mentioned again on later pages.

Attention has been drawn to the origin of monasticism
at the beginning of this period. The work of St. Pachomius
in Egypt was extended (p. 26), and by the beginning of the
fifth century the monks of his order had become numerous;
the Skētē Desert and the Natron Lakes became an important
monastic centre. But in Egypt the movement began to lose
force towards the close of the century, and its decline was
hastened by the Arab conquest. The common life instituted
by Pachomius was introduced into Syria and the neighbouring
regions early in the fourth century. Probably the eremitic life
had been led in Syria before this date; and even after the establishment of monasteries its greater austerity continued to
recommend it to the Syrian temperament. But in the second
half of the fourth century St. Basil of Caesarea in Cappadocia
adapted the principles of Pachomius to Greek conditions, and
instituted a rule which for a long time afterwards remained in
the ascendant throughout the Christian East. It discouraged
extreme asceticism, and, like that of St. Benedict, approved
intellectual as well as manual labour. In the West, monasticism had been introduced into Italy after the visit of
St. Athanasius to Rome in A.D. 340. It first developed after
the eremitic fashion of the earlier recluses in Egypt, but the
lack of cohesion which resulted led to the establishment by
St. Benedict, about A.D. 500, of a rule which remained without
a rival in Latin monasticism for several centuries; the great
monastery of Monte Cassino between Rome and Naples was
founded by St. Benedict. Special mention may be made of
the two monasteries at Squillace in Bruttii, founded in the
second half of the sixth century by Cassiodorus, ex-minister of
the Ostrogothic King Theodoric. Cassiodorus was acquainted
with the work of the theological schools in the Christian
East; he specially insisted on the importance of transcribing manuscripts, and doubtless illumination was also practised.
In Gaul monasteries were erected from the close of the
fourth century. The most famous were those of St. Honoratus,
on one of the islands of Lérins off the south coast; of
St. Victor at Marseilles; that at Poitiers; and those of

PLATE III. IVORY PANEL: THE BAPTISM. SIXTH CENTURY.

Marmoutier and St. Martin in Touraine; at Marseilles and at
Lérins there were schools which contributed to the preservation of classical learning. The monasteries of Gaul were
closely connected with the early Christianity of the British
Isles and of Ireland. The name of St. Ninian is associated
with that of St. Martin; those of St. Patrick and St. Augustine
with the monastery of Lérins. Gaul was the chief scene of
Columban's missionary work at the close of the sixth century.
The Irish rule of eremitic tendency, introduced by him at
three monasteries in the neighbourhood of the Vosges, was
widely spread by his disciples, but it could not resist the
growth of the Benedictine system, and was almost forgotten
by the time of Charles the Great.

Fig. 19.—Section of dome-shaped silver casket, Esquiline Treasure.
(No. 305.)

These centuries embraced the first great period of the
Byzantine Empire, culminating in the reign of Justinian, a
time of activity for all the arts, from architecture and mosaic
to the weaving of silk (p. 150) or the manufacture of jewellery
and silver plate; in this reign Italy was for a short time
recovered by Byzantine arms, and the city of Ravenna enriched
by buildings still standing to attest the splendour of the age.

The eastern provinces enjoyed a comparative tranquillity until
the close of the reign, and a prosperity enhanced by the introduction of the silkworm from Central Asia. After Justinian the
rivalry of the East-Roman Empire and Persia drew to a head,
and exhausting wars ensued in which the emperor Heraclius
bore a victorious part, avenging the capture of Jerusalem by the

Persians in A.D. 614, when Constantine's Church of the Holy Sepulchre was destroyed. The number of works of art surviving from the sixth century, not only on the large scale in the form of church buildings with their mosaics, but on the small in the shape of manuscripts, ivory carvings, textiles, silver plate, and jewellery, attests the prosperity enjoyed in this period by Egypt, Syria, and Asia Minor. But at the time of Heraclius's death in A.D. 641 the Arabs were already overrunning Egypt and the loss of the first two of these provinces was imminent. We have seen that despite certain oriental influences Rome had preserved the tradition of her earlier Christian art down to the end of the reign of Theodoric (p. 28). The ensuing war of more than twenty years between the Goths and the Byzantine armies brought ruin and depopulation to the city, and a complete end to its old life. Its new inhabitants after the peace were in great part orientals. A Byzantine governor lived on the Palatine; eastern monasteries were established, and even Gregory the Great, a Roman born, entrusted his own monastery on the Caelian to Greek monks. From the latter part of the sixth century began an orientalizing period in Rome, lasting for about two hundred years. It was precisely the time when the city, raised by the Popes to the position of a great spiritual capital, drew to itself more and more the homage of the western world. This was a coincidence not without its effect upon the development of European mediaeval art (p. 43).

In Gaul Roman rule ended in Provence in A.D. 475, the Visigoths and the Burgundians holding the country south of the Loire; the Franks occupied the north-west; to the north-east Syagrius maintained his Gallo-Roman kingdom until overthrown by the Franks in A.D. 486. The Visigoths and Burgundians were already Christians. Both were amenable in their degree to civilization, tolerant of the Gallo-Roman culture and themselves practising various arts; the Visigoths are held by some to have built stone churches. The tranquillity of Gaul enabled monasticism to make more progress here than elsewhere, and to do much for education: the influence of Gaulish monasteries was of great importance to Britain and Ireland, with which countries communications were maintained (p. 35). The Franks, converted to (Catholic) Christianity in A.D. 496, were of a rougher mould than the Goths, but they too were skilled in certain minor arts. In A.D. 507 Clovis, their first Christian king, defeated the Visigoths, and the Frankish monarchy soon extended over the whole country. Under the descendants of Clovis the land was divided into several kingdoms, and the sixth century was a period of domestic feud and general insecurity. Nevertheless churches and monasteries were built, including a new abbey church of St. Martin at Tours, and there are allusions to paintings with which some of them were adorned. As related above (p. 31), Merovingian kings were patrons of national art chiefly in the form of goldsmiths' and silversmiths' work; for, as in Constantinople, workshops were attached to the royal palaces, in which ornaments, plate, and perhaps textile fabrics were produced for the use of the court.

A great part of Spain had been held by the Visigoths before their defeat in Gaul in A.D. 507, though the Suevi were established in the north-west. After that event Spain became the sole Visigothic kingdom, though from A.D. 554 to A.D. 629 the Byzantine Empire held a considerable region in the south and south-east. In A.D. 587 King Recared abandoned Arianism to become a Catholic, but the people to a great extent adhered to their traditional faith. As in Gaul, the state of the country was disturbed by political divisions, and by strife between the nobles and the kings, but this did not prevent a considerable development of the arts. A

FIG. 20.—Terracotta lamp with the story of Jonah. (No. 718.)

great deal of building took place during the Visigothic period, but though parts of various churches have been ascribed to Visigothic architects, the limits of their work are ill defined. Complete churches exemplifying their supposed tradition actually date from the ninth century and are later than the conquest of the country by the Arabs. It may be said here by way of anticipation that while some believe Visigothic architectural methods to have come directly from the East at the time of the great migrations, others hold that in a country like Spain, where the Latin influence was very strong, they could not but continue the Roman tradition.

Visigothic minor arts are best known by the gold votive crowns from Guarrazar enriched with *orfévrerie cloisonnée* now in Madrid and in the Musée de Cluny at Paris; they show that in the seventh century the old Persian style was still being practised in Spain.

North-west Africa, which had been under direct Roman influence during the early Christian centuries, was taken by the Vandals in A.D. 435, and for about a hundred years was oppressed by the Vandal kings. The conquest of the country for Justinian by Belisarius in A.D. 533 led to the construction of fortresses and public buildings, but the ecclesiastical architecture of the country as a whole seems to have depended chiefly upon Roman tradition. The Byzantine government was harsh and unpopular, and the arrival of the Mohammedan invaders found the people ready for a change of rulers. Thus in A.D. 709 the last bulwark of Christianity in Northern Africa was overthrown by Islam.

For the British Isles during this period see pp. 56–61.

Fig. 21.—Terracotta lamp from Syria. (No. 835.)

We may review the principal characteristics of these centuries as a period in the development of Christian art. They witnessed a complete change from the symbolism of the earlier age to a system of historical and dogmatic representation. The change came about because the freed Church wished to employ art to celebrate its triumph and set forth its creed: the close relations between a centralized Church and the imperial court led also to the glorification by artistic means of the imperial power. Under the new conditions the positive Syrian spirit gained ground at the expense of the Greek, though for practical reasons it was compelled to accept

Hellenistic aid. There thus arose a new Christian sacred art, composed of two main factors, Syrian and Greek, the relative strength of which varied according to environment, the Greek element being strong in the Hellenistic cities and in the Byzantine capital, weak in the inland countries and in the

FIG. 22.—Pottery vase with two faces, Wadi Sarga.

monasteries which, intellectually influenced from Edessa and Nisibis, had commonly some oriental bias. Thus the general tendency was one of orientalization down to the late sixth century, at which time the full stream of eastern influence began flowing into an exhausted Rome. A Syro-Hellenistic figure art accompanied by conventionalized ornament, originally, it may be supposed, of Persian descent, was thus the art which dominated the Europe of the so-called Dark Ages; it was the missionary art of a monasticism oriental in spirit and always maintaining relations with the East. Less scientific and franker in emotion than unmodified Greek art, less concerned also with exact imitation of nature, it appealed to the barbaric peoples as Hellenic art had never done, partly because, even in its representation, it was affected by consideration of abstract design.

It was a definitely Christian art, a new thing. It has sometimes been maintained that Early Christian Art was nothing but the shadow of classical art, absorbed in the deepening gloom of barbarism. So far is this from the fact, that the very time of its presumed extinction marked its emergence into a vigorous maturity. The error has arisen from too narrow a limitation of the view, and a tendency to overlook the dominant part played at this time by the countries east of the Mediterranean. There may be difference of opinion as to the quality of this art, but as to its vitality there can be none. No shadowy survival could have nourished and brought up the infant art of Europe during several hundred years.

c. *From the Arab Conquests to the end of Iconoclasm in* A.D. 842.

The period of decline through which the Byzantine Empire passed after the reign of Justinian was relieved by the victory of Heraclius over the Persians; but with the Arab invasion and the outbreak of the iconoclastic dispute the tide reached its lowest ebb. North Africa was overrun, and the Eastern territories reduced by the loss of Syria and Egypt, the two provinces which had contributed so much to the formation of Christian art.

Iconoclasm, which in practice signified rather the defacement or destruction of religious paintings than the breaking of images, began in A.D. 726 under the Emperor Leo III, and lasted more than a hundred years. In contrasting their own humiliation with the triumph of the Arabs, men remembered that the faith of the victors forbade the representation of the divine form; they began to associate their military disasters with the excessive veneration of ikons which had especially flourished under monastic influence; the patriotic were already indignant at the system which in the hour of danger refused thousands of able-bodied monks to the imperial armies. Much of the strength of the movement was derived from the people upon the eastern borders, where the Persian dislike for sacred pictures, approved in general by Armenia, was known and in great measure shared; and since this feeling was in the Iranian region accompanied by a preference for a non-representational art of ornament, aesthetic causes were linked from the first with religious. The iconoclastic dispute became a matter of art no less than of religion; it resolved itself into a long struggle to oust representation, and to substitute for the didactic pictures of Syria the pure

FIG. 23.—A design on a terracotta plate from Egypt. (No. 926.)

ornament of Iran. Thus aesthetic principle was involved with religious questions throughout the interminable conflict, and the art which avoided the reproduction of nature seemed often near to success. But victory finally remained with picture-worship and with the Syro-Hellenistic representational art which was supported by the whole strength of monasticism; it was left to Islam, which had never known representation, to develop an art of decoration to its logical extreme. The end of iconoclasm, in A.D. 842, marked not only a victory for the Orthodox Church, but for sacred representational art within the Empire. Yet the defeated side had not fought without effect. A wave of orientalism brought with it new motives, geometrical, animal, and floral, and many of these found a permanent place in East-Christian design. The resemblance between Saracenic and later Byzantine ornament is often striking, because both come in the main from the same Persian source; but whereas the former enjoyed the fullest independence, the latter was subordinated to figure subjects. Armenian sympathy with the iconoclastic struggle is emphasized by the fact that more than one of the iconoclast emperors were of Armenian descent, and in the attitude which they adopted probably represented the prevalent opinion in their native country. The Armenian Church had indeed accepted a sacred figure art under Syrian influence; but it would seem that although this found approval among the clergy, the people in general disliked sacred representation. Armenians sat on the imperial throne after iconoclasm had come to an end; and Basil I, who was of that race, inaugurated in A. D. 867 a new political and artistic period of Byzantine history, in which Armenian influences can often be discerned.

The attitude of the Arabs to Christianity in the conquered provinces varied under different dynasties, but as a rule those Christians who refused to change their faith were tolerated, though placed under restrictions as regards dress, the building of churches, and other matters. Thus monasteries in Egypt, Palestine, and Syria pursued their existence and maintained relations with the religious houses still within the Byzantine Empire; pilgrimage to the Holy Land, though sometimes interrupted, continued under the Mohammedan rule. For some time during the first half of the period, the Caliphate was held by the Ummayads (A. D. 661–750), who represented the old Arab aristocracy, and were not in full sympathy with the teaching of Mohammed. These rulers were not fanatical in religion, and were tolerant of other creeds. Their capital was Damascus, and they were great patrons of the fine arts, not refusing aid from artists or craftsmen of any race able to gratify their tastes, and willing in their buildings to adopt forms used by Christians; thus the Caliph Abd El-Malek (A. D. 685–705) rebuilt a church of Justinian at Jerusalem on basilican lines as the mosque El-Aksa. For the ornamentation of the interiors they used mosaic, and when, *c.* A. D. 708, the Caliph Walīd (A. D. 705–15) adapted the pre-existing Christian church at Damascus for use as a mosque, he asked the Byzantine Emperor for mosaic cubes to carry out the decoration.

In the desert palace of Quseir 'Amra, probably built for a prince of this line, the walls are painted with figure-subjects, some of which are Hellenistic in character. With the accession of the Abbāsid dynasty (A.D. 750–1258) the capital was removed to Baghdad, and Mohammedan art passed more definitely under Persian control, though the development attained by the Copts of Egypt was naturally influential in the South. A period of increased orthodoxy was accompanied by a magnificence of decorative design, such as might naturally be expected when the capital of Islam was moved within the Persian sphere. Under the Abbāsids, a non-representational decorative style, chiefly of Persian derivation, was henceforward typical of Mohammedan expression, as Syro-Hellenistic representation was typical of Byzantine sacred art. Two opposing systems were firmly established; though in the course of centuries often influencing each other, they remained severally characteristic of Christianity and of Islam.

While the peaceful development of the Christian East was interrupted by foreign invasion and internal dispute, the West was for the most part disturbed by the first cause alone. The Arabs conquered North Africa and Spain. The Lombards, driving out the last Byzantine exarchs from Ravenna, harassed the papacy to such an extent that they brought about their own overthrow. In A.D. 774 Stephen II, in despair of effective aid from Constantinople, appealed to Pepin king of the Franks, and the help then given confirmed relations which resulted in the final defeat of the Lombards, the coronation of Pepin's son Charles the Great as Emperor (A.D. 800), and the final severance of official relations between Constantinople and Rome. But the West was not drawn into the devastating iconoclastic struggle. It had not carried picture-worship to the same lengths as the East; neither Rome nor the Frankish Kings accepted the iconoclastic doctrine. The consequence was that in Italy and the West the development of Christian art proceeded tranquilly upon the old lines; the Syro-Hellenistic sacred art of the preceding period was secure in a Rome now full of Eastern monasteries and ruled by many Syrian popes, from Theodore, a Greek of Jerusalem (A.D. 642) to Zacharias (A.D. 741). The mural paintings on the walls of the ruined church of St. Maria Antiqua below the Palatine Hill, or on those of St. Saba, attest the continuance of a style introduced after the Gothic wars, but confirmed by an influx of Greek fugitives from iconoclasm in A.D. 726, and from Ravenna after the capture of that city by the Lombards in A.D. 752. The minor arts were influenced from the same sources, as we learn from the interesting discovery made at the beginning of the present century in the chapel of the Sancta Sanctorum at the Lateran, the last surviving part of the mediaeval palace. Here a number of reliquaries and other objects were preserved in a chest contained within the altar, originally deposited by Pope Leo III (A.D. 795–816), and untouched since the time of Leo X (A.D. 1513–21). The contents, now preserved in the Vatican Library, included several objects of East-Christian workmanship dating from before the Arab invasions; among them were an enamelled gold cruciform reliquary of the sixth or early seventh century with New Testament scenes of which the iconography points to Syria-Palestine, and fine fragments of figured silk, one with the Annunciation and the Nativity of rather earlier date, probably made at Alexandria, with other textiles having Persian designs. Such were the more precious examples of the industrial arts entering the Rome of the early Middle Ages. It need not, however, be supposed that Rome remained merely receptive. As in the period before Constantine Hellenistic artists from Alexandria must have trained many Italian pupils, as down to the Gothic wars a Roman monumental art still persisted, so in this later Rome the artists from Syria or Egypt must have found Italian followers and rivals: we seem to mark in some of the Roman frescoes painted in these centuries, oriental though they are in general character, a feeling which is not wholly of the East. It is held by some that an Italian hand may have produced at Rome the interesting miniatures painted on the inner surfaces of the diptych of the Consul Boethius now at Brescia, at the time, perhaps in the early part of the seventh century, when this secular diptych was adapted to liturgical uses. The style recalls that of such illuminated books as the

Fig. 24.—Terracotta lamp, probably from Egypt. (No 822.)

sixth-century Gospels at Rossano (p. 122), and, if the theory is correct, these miniatures, like the mural paintings, show us a native Italian art striving to emerge under East-Christian inspiration. Yet it was probably less as a creative than as a distributive centre that in these obscure times Rome best served the interests of Christian art. From this partly oriental city Augustine set out in A.D. 597 upon his English Mission; from Rome in the second half of the following century Benedict Biscop of Jarrow and St. Wilfrid introduced ecclesiastical works of art into Northumbria; the models for the reliefs on the high crosses of Ruthwell and Bewcastle, though probably themselves of East-Christian inspiration, may well have reached Britain through the intermediary of Rome from some more distant source (p. 66). With Benedict in A.D. 669 Theodore of Tarsus, an inmate of an eastern monastery in Rome, came to England to occupy the See of Canterbury. The eighth century saw the oriental influence at its height, and its reaction on the West assured by the increasing settlements in Rome of Lombards, Franks, and Anglo-Saxons. Our countrymen had a quarter of their own, with a church and hospice endowed by Ina, King of Wessex, in A.D. 728. When the papacy was allied to the new Frankish Empire, and political relations with Byzantium were broken off, eastern influence began to decline, and for a while it seemed that a new Italian art might come into being. But Rome was not yet ready, and the decreasing strength of the oriental element was not compensated by a vigorous growth of native art. The Carolingian Empire was divided, and Rome suffered from the insecurity and confusion following upon its decay. After the first quarter of the ninth century, her art fell to a depth which it had never reached before.

In northern Italy the arts continued largely under Teutonic domination. Enamelling, which the ancient Romans had practised in the champlevé form, appeared in Italy perhaps as early as the late sixth century, but in the cloisonné variety in favour throughout the East; features of an early example in the Museum collections (p. 145) suggest that this craft may have been exercised by Ostrogoths or by orientals working for them, and may have been handed on in this manner to the Lombards; several examples of enamelling in Italy during the ninth century are preserved (p. 145). The Lombards were in a less advanced state of civilization than the Goths; but in the two centuries of their dominion in Italy they developed considerable skill in decorative art, especially

46 INTRODUCTION

in sculpture, the motives commonly suggesting an Eastern descent.

In Gaul this period embraces the latter part of the Merovingian (earlier Frankish), and the earlier part of the Carolingian (later Frankish) age which began with

FIG. 25.—Fragments of painted pottery, Wadi Sarga : sixth century.

Charles the Great (A.D. 768–814). Here, as in Italy, Eastern influences were conspicuous. Certain Merovingian illuminated initials in MSS. ascribed to the eighth century have capitals formed of birds and fish which find remarkable parallels in the Christian East; while the formal ornament which accompanies or frames the earliest Carolingian miniatures probably came with these from Syria and Egypt. The gospels of the monk Godescalc, in the National Library at Paris, executed for Charles the Great in A.D. 781–783, have illustration directly based on the art of Syrian illuminated books of the sixth century, such as the Gospels now at Edgmiatsin in Armenia, and the Gospels of Rabula in Florence (p. 122). A like Syrian inspiration may be observed in other Carolingian illuminated MSS., and it may be recalled that Charles availed himself of the aid of Syrian monks in his emendation of the gospel text. The well-known Utrecht Psalter, with its sensitive line drawings, is, on the other hand, based upon a lost Hellenistic model of more ancient date and probably of Alexandrian origin, showing that late Greek art was not without its appeal to the Western illuminator of this period. Carolingian ivory carvings naturally reveal the same Eastern and Hellenistic influences as the manuscripts. Among the collection in the British Museum (King Edward VII gallery, Pier Case, Bay XX) is, for example, a *pyxis* of ivory carved with New Testament subjects in imitation of earlier work from Egypt or Syria, like that seen on a pyxis in the same case carved with the martyrdom of St. Menas. The Victoria and Albert Museum has an ivory book-cover in which, in the same way, an East-Christian model is reproduced by a Carolingian artist. Enamelling, which as above noted had also revived in Italy, was practised from the close of the early Carolingian period, not only in the cloisonné, but also in the champlevé variety.

In Spain the Mohammedans overthrew the Visigothic Kingdom in A.D. 711. They found in the country an art which, on its decorative side, had a similar Eastern origin to their own (p. 38); the resemblance between the designs on fragments of decorative sculpture assigned to the Visigothic period and Coptic and Syrian ornament has often been remarked; decoration showing these affinities and based on palmette or vine motives lasted for a long time in the peninsula, and outlived Moorish times.

Summing up this period, we find it a decisive epoch in the history of earlier Christian art. In the East it marked the restoration of sacred figure art and the rejection of the non-representational expression which triumphed in the countries conquered by Islam. If the Arabs had not stopped short at Asia Minor; if Charles Martel had not driven them back from central France in A.D. 732, the style and methods of mediaeval and later art might have been very different from those which we know; the condition of European art as a whole might have approximated in various degrees to that of Spain under the Moors. As it was, the Byzantine and the Frankish armies stayed the advance of Islam. In the West the sacred figure art of Syro-Hellenistic descent (p. 28) was left to provide models undisturbed for Italian and Frankish artists. At Rome, which had rejected iconoclasm, the increased influence of the papacy was synchronous with the spread of oriental monastic art. Rome had become a centre of unrivalled importance; it contained colonies of Franks and Anglo-Saxons, and was visited by western ecclesiastics like Benedict Biscop, who took home with them for their own churches works of art brought to the city of the Popes from all parts of the Christian world.

After the establishment of a new Empire by Charles the Great, East-Christian influence upon Western Europe continued, but had not quite the same vital importance as in the early centuries, when the art of a continent under barbaric dominion owed its development to East-Christian aid: the peoples of Europe now owed more to their own activities. But for a long time it still permeated European art; to its presence we may ascribe in no small degree the cosmopolitan nature of the art which we call Romanesque.

d. *From the end of Iconoclasm to the Fourth Crusade of* A.D. 1204.

With the accession of Basil I (A.D. 867–886) there began a period which may more accurately be styled Byzantine than any which had gone before. The mere reduction of the Empire, and the loss of Syria and Egypt, with their great intellectual and artistic centres of Antioch and Alexandria, increased the relative importance of Constantinople and Salonika. And during the first two hundred years of the period the Byzantine arms were once more victorious, overthrowing the Bulgarian kingdom, and pushing forward in the East into Armenia and Georgia; as the early movements of the Seljūks disturbed the Caliphate, the prestige of Constantinople increased while that of the Abbāsids weakened. Success quickened national sentiment and reacted favourably upon all creative work. At the same time friendly relations were maintained with the western emperors, one of whom, Otto II, married a Byzantine princess. Envoys passed between the courts, and as in earlier times, gifts in the form of works of art were exchanged; the East-Roman Empire occupied a great place in

HISTORICAL SURVEY 49

the world, and its restored prosperity was worthily reflected in its art. But at the close of the eleventh century the prospect was again darkened by the battle of Malazgerd (Manzikert) on the borders of Armenia, in which the Emperor Romanus was defeated and taken prisoner by the Seljūk Turk, Alp Arslan, in A.D. 1071. This year may be regarded as

Fig. 26.—Fragments of painted pottery, Wadi Sarga : sixth century.

a turning-point, after which the fortunes of the Empire declined. As the Turks increased their hold on Asia Minor, the prosperity of Byzantium was exchanged for comparative poverty; the arts which had flowered during the expansion of national life now withered under its depression.

The first century of the two hundred years of success was

marked in Constantinople by a certain renewal of Greek influence, sometimes called the neo-classical revival. During iconoclasm the secular art, largely mythological, which had always flourished in the capital under aristocratic patronage, extended its scope. The Hellenistic movement profited so much from the attack upon pictures that after the re-establishment of peace in the Church it was able for a long time to extend its influence over religious art. Many miniatures in illuminated books and many ivory carvings of the tenth century (p. 125) are distinguished by a refined and almost classical style in which we sometimes seem to discern a Hellenic rather than a Hellenistic quality. But the monastic influences which had won the victory over iconoclasm gradually renewed their strength; ecclesiastical control was drawn closer; religious art was more intimately connected with the liturgical Feasts of the Christian Year. The iconography of the Syrian period, still preserved in the monasteries of Cappadocia, became once more a source of inspiration; sacred art, with its new ritual associations, became graver and more austere in proportion as the monastic spirit was asserted: thus in the mosaics of St. Luke of Stiris in Phocis the oriental spirit is more marked than in those of Daphni in Attica, where the Hellenistic element is exceptionally strong. In Constanti-

Fig. 27.—Byzantine gilt bronze plaque: St. Theodore: eleventh century. (No. 544.)

nople Hellenism never wholly lost the position which it had attained in the tenth century; through the first hundred years of what may be called the liturgical period, when Byzantium produced admirable works of art both on the monumental and on the diminutive scale, its influence is still apparent. The churches of this time are distinguished by logical construction and a fine sense of decorative values, while the architects brought to perfection the cruciform type (p. 95) best suited to their own genius and the requirements of their age. Illumination and ivory carving on the highest level of achievement attest the notable standard of execution prevailing at the time; both arts were instrumental in forming the reviving sculpture of the West, and thus possessed a significance out of proportion to the scale on which they worked. In other minor arts, such as those of weaving and enamelling, oriental influences are conspicuous, and the silk fabrics are reminiscent of the Sassanian style; here again inspiration was given to the West (p. 150).

Through all this time East-Christian and Byzantine influence continued to be felt in Italy, south Germany, and France. In Rome, indeed, harassed by Saracenic invasion and feudal disturbances, art remained at a low ebb until the end of the eleventh century. But elsewhere in Italy conditions were more favourable. The monasteries still played the most important part in the reproduction and distribution of illuminated MSS. and in the provision of designs for mural paintings, in both ways stimulating the native art of the western countries. Eastern monasticism was actually at home in Italy, especially in Calabria and Apulia. Here a large community of Basilian monks, augmented by refugees from iconoclasm, decorated their rock-cut cells and chapels with eastern frescoes not superseded by Italian work until a later period in the Middle Ages. At the beginning of the eleventh century St. Nilus, a Basilian from the south, founded the abbey of Grottaferrata near Rome; while the great Benedictine House of Monte Cassino introduced Byzantine mosaic-workers in the same century. As in earlier times, commerce, like monasticism, continued to spread the knowledge of oriental art. Venice became a powerful state, and its relations with Constantinople affected the style and decoration of its buildings. The cathedral of St. Mark's reproduced the plan of the Church of the Apostles at Constantinople, and its original mosaic decoration, of which only parts now remain, was East-Christian in subject, that of the narthex copying an early Bible of the type of the

Cotton Genesis (p. 122). Other cities, Pisa and Genoa, followed the lead of Venice as maritime powers; the increase of their commerce with the Eastern Mediterranean led them in like manner to adopt oriental features in their art: at Pisa the arcaded decoration of the cathedral and the baptistery betray the influence of the East. In German mural painting and illumination we mark a general permeation of monastic art by Byzantine influences rather than exact copying of particular models. This was the manner in which, during these later centuries, the West absorbed Eastern teaching; the peoples, conscious of their own powers, were now creative, and a general guidance began to satisfy their needs.

The conversion of Vladimir in the last quarter of the tenth century led to the introduction of Byzantine and Armenian art into the south of Russia; the building of the earliest

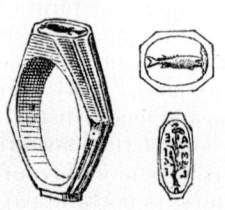

FIG. 28.—Gold ring engraved with a fish. (No. 48.)

FIG. 29.—Gold finger-ring with sacred monogram. (No. 28.)

monastic houses on Mount Athos in the tenth century created a new centre of East-Christian art in the Balkans, where the establishment of national monasteries—Greek, Serbian, Georgian, Russian—made the peninsula a meeting-place for influences from various countries. In the latter part of the period the Norman Kings of Sicily decorated churches at Palermo, Monreale, and Cefalù in the north of the island with mosaics in the Byzantine style, and introduced silk-weavers from Greece. The western rulers of Jerusalem employed East-Christian artists to adorn churches with mosaic, as at Bethlehem, and illuminate manuscripts (cf. the Psalter of Queen Melisenda in the Grenville Library, Case 8).

To resume the substance of the above paragraphs: this period, which includes the reigns of the Comnenian Emperors, witnessed the rise and decline of a great Byzantine art. Churches, admirably planned and constructed, were decorated with mosaics equalling in splendour those of the time of Justinian; illuminations, ivory carvings, enamels, silk fabrics set the western world a high standard of craftsmanship from which it did not fail to profit. The Greek element was prominent even in the religious art of the capital, though in Cappadocian and other monasteries the old Syro-Hellenistic influences remained powerful. The earlier part of the period is a Byzantine golden age, in which the capital had a more creative share in the art of the Empire than in the time before the Arab Conquest, and a greater name in the West of Europe.

e. *From the fourth Crusade to the capture of Constantinople by the Turks* (A.D. 1204–1453).

The Latin interregnum of about sixty years beginning with the seizure of Constantinople in A.D. 1204 was a time of unsettlement disastrous to art in the capital; Byzantine civilization took refuge at Nicaea and Trebizond, and Byzantine artists in increased numbers seem to have migrated to Venice or sought the patronage of the now powerful Serbian Kings. The invasion of Byzantine territory by Western forces dislocated the organization of the arts; only in remote and undisturbed monasteries could the old traditions of religious art be pursued, and many of these were beyond the borders of the empire, in Egypt, Syria, and the Holy Land.

The immediate effects of the Latin occupation were disastrous to Constantinople not merely through the break in old tradition, but through the greed and barbarism of the invaders, who broke and melted down objects of metal, and divided as spoil the contents of the church treasuries which they had plundered. In some ways, however, the closer contact between the Italians and the Greeks may have brought compensations. The enlarged activities of Byzantine panel-painters in northern and Central Italy is reflected in the art of the earliest Italian primitives; on the other hand, something of the fresh Italian spirit was transmitted to the Greeks, introducing more grace, breadth, and natural feeling. The work of the Byzantine painters in Serbia shows signs of this influence, which is also seen in that of their Serbian pupils.

The restoration of the Greek Empire in A.D. 1261 was followed by a period of activity in art and letters, quickened by a last revival of national sentiment, and a desire to assert once more the Greek culture which had been so rudely interrupted. The restored Empire was poor; only by rare exception, as in the case of the Church of the Chora at Constantinople, now the Mosque Kahrieh Jami, could costly mosaic be employed. In the capital, where the Latin interference had been strongest, there seems to have been a certain incoherence; an art, forced to copy models not wholly understood, derived its elements from incompatible sources and created effects which are

Fig. 30.—Gold ring with openwork inscription. (No. 49.)

picturesque, but result in a confusion of styles. Elsewhere, as in Mistra, the capital of the newly-constituted Byzantine province in the Morea, we seem to find the continuity of art better preserved, perhaps through a more direct association with the schools of painting which had been developing in Macedonia and Serbia, Crete, and Venice (p. 119). Though

Fig. 31.— Gold marriage-ring. Fifth century. (No. 207)

ornamental sculpture flourished, figure sculpture is but little represented. Some examples, like the relief with angels dating from this time in the above-named church of the Chora, may show an influence from the West.

Objects illustrating the minor arts are rarer than in the preceding period. Costly work, such as that of the enameller and the goldsmith, was naturally less common; embroidery

on silk took the place of fabrics within woven designs. In the
final years, when emperors themselves were reduced to poverty,
there was little patronage and little scope for any arts of
luxury. The conquest of Constantinople in A.D. 1453 closes
the history of Byzantine art in the stricter sense of the term.
But its influence, and that of the East-Christian elements
allied to it, continued in various places long after the fall of
the Empire; thus its traditions survived in the sacred art of
Greece and the Balkans, Russia, Armenia, and Coptic Egypt;
they were preserved above all in the monasteries, and notably
in those of Mount Athos, where mural paintings in the style of
the Cretan school were produced during the sixteenth century
(p. 120).

Except in the case of panel painting, the art of this period

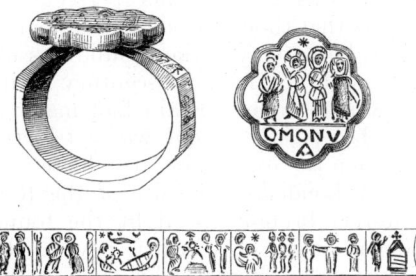

Fig. 32.—Byzantine gold marriage-ring with ornament in niello. About
tenth century. (No. 129.)

exerted little or no influence upon Europe west of the Adriatic.
With Cavallini and Giotto, Italian art entered upon a new
career; with the rise of Gothic, Western Europe began to tread
fresh paths; by degrees the debt owed to East-Christian art
was forgotten. Even to-day there is still a tendency to treat
the whole of our earlier mediaeval art as an independent
growth, for the understanding of which no knowledge of the
Christian East is required. So far is this from being the case,
that during the seven centuries between the fourth and the
twelfth, every country in Europe from Italy to Ireland was
helped by East-Christian models in its effort after artistic
expression, and but for that help our art could not have
developed as it did. The Christian art of the West and that
of the East are parts of an organic whole, nor can they be
studied apart without vital loss. No full appreciation of early
mediaeval art is possible without the recognition of this fact.

PART II. SPECIAL SECTIONS

I. Early Christianity in Britain.

It is probable that there were Christian communities in Britain early in the third century; passages in Tertullian and Origen, both writing in the first half of that century, allow us to infer this with some certainty. The Greek historians Eusebius and Sozomen, writing in the fourth and fifth centuries respectively, further relate that under the government of Constantius Chlorus, father of the Emperor Constantine and governor of the Gauls, Spain, and Britain (*d.* York, A.D. 300), the Christians in Britain were not persecuted; Lactantius (*d.* A.D. 325) adds that though Constantius spared the persons of the Christians he destroyed their buildings (*conventicula*). Thus the statement of the sixth-century British historian Gildas that in Roman times Britain had many churches was always credible, but positive proof was not forthcoming until the year 1892, when the excavations conducted by the Society of Antiquaries of London on the site of the Roman town of Calleva (Silchester) brought to light the foundations of a church, the Roman origin of which is beyond dispute (p. 61). Very little is known of British Christians in Roman times; the name of St. Alban of Verulam, martyred in A.D. 304, has come down to us almost alone with those of the bishops Eborius, Restitutus, and Adelfius, who represented the British Episcopate at the Council held at Arles in A.D. 314. But it is clear that the community must have been numerous, for when St. Germanus and St. Lupus were in Britain between the departure of the Romans in A.D. 410 and the Saxon invasion of about A.D. 450, it is related that the concourse of people coming to hear them was very great, not only in the churches, but at cross-roads, in the country districts and in remote places. We infer from Gildas that after the time of Constantine, when the British church obtained toleration, the stricter observances of the first three centuries became relaxed, and a certain reaction set in, as it had done in other countries. This period of comparative inactivity, only stirred for a while by the Pelagian heresy, remained undisturbed until a long time after the departure of the Romans; the Mission of St. Ninian (*c.* A.D. 400), a Briton who had been in Rome and had also come under the influence of Gaulish monasticism, affected only

PLATE IV. IVORY BOXES OF THE SIXTH CENTURY: DANIEL IN THE DEN OF LIONS, AND THE MARTYRDOM OF ST. MENAS.

(*See* p. 169.)

a small area beyond the Roman lines in the country of the Southern Picts (now Galloway), and may be regarded as an isolated exception: in Gaul Ninian was probably connected with St. Martin, to whom he dedicated his stone church at Whitherne, or Whithorn (p. 62). In the second quarter of the fifth century an event occurred which was destined to interrupt the quiet life of the Church not only in Britain but ultimately on the continent; this was the coming of St. Patrick to Ireland. St. Patrick, whose original name was Sucat, was the son of Calpornius, a deacon of the Church, also holding the office of decurion or local councillor under the Roman system; his grandfather, Potitus, had been a *presbyter* or priest. At the close of the fourth century, or the very beginning of the fifth, Patrick was carried off by Irish raiders from his home at a place called 'ad Bannavem taberniae', not certainly identified: some authorities believe it to have been Dumbarton, others have suggested Banwen in Glamorganshire. Sold as a slave in Ireland, he remained in that country six years, when he escaped into Gaul, studying at Marmoutiers, at Auxerre under St. Germanus, and in the great monastic school on the island of Lérins off the south coast. He then proceeded to Rome and obtained the approval of Pope Celestine for his proposed mission to Ireland, which he was able to carry out in A.D. 437 or 438. St. Patrick at once roused the fervour of the Irish and introduced among them the ascetic form of Christianity practised in the monasteries of Gaul. He adapted the monastic system to the needs of the country, making the monasteries the centres of religious life, and in many cases attaching bishops to them so that the bishop was in effect controlled by the abbot; it has been said that ' the monastery with its abbot was for the clergy what the clan with its chief was for the laity '. But more important than the form of Irish monasticism were its fervid, ascetic spirit and its missionary zeal, to which we shall almost immediately return.

When in the middle of the fifth century the pagan Saxons extended their foothold in the south of England, the majority of the Christian Britons concentrated their strength in the west under the native Kings of Damnonia (Devon and Cornwall), most of whom were Christian; their Church was organized on Roman lines with diocesan bishops and clergy, remaining part of the Western Patriarchate. But a large number crossed the Channel to Armorica (Brittany), a part of Gaul which had itself been so ravaged by the Saxons that its previous population was almost wholly destroyed. The British immigrants were reinforced by later groups, and finally became so numerous that they gradually filled this depopulated region, making their tongue the language of the country. The settlements began in the western and central parts of the peninsula, and by the ninth century covered the territory known since the arrival of the British as Brittany. Clergy and people came over in large bodies, and territory, once administered, in part at least, by the Gallo-Roman Church, was now to all intents and purposes British.

While this colonization of Brittany was in progress, the Irish Church under the disciples of St. Patrick began, towards the beginning of the sixth century, a series of missions to the west shores of the British Isles, extending from Wales in the middle to the Scottish coast in the north and to Cornwall in

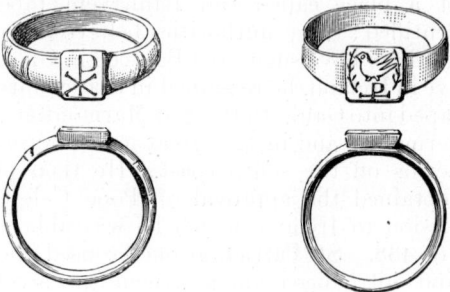

Figs. 33, 34.—Two rings from Fifehead Neville, Dorsetshire, with sacred monogram: fourth century.

the south. Irish missionaries began to pour into the west of Britain from the Clyde to Cornwall, introducing a new element into the British Church. Probably the earliest Irish mission proceeded to Wales, and some of the later missions active farther to the south may be described as Irish-Welsh rather than purely Irish. A large part in the new missionary activity was played by the family which gave Brecon its name, tracing its descent to the eponymous Brychan Brycheiniog, son of Anlach Goronog, described in the Welsh Genealogies of the Saints as 'King of Ireland'; this family was connected by marriage with the house of Cunedda, to which St. David belonged, and also with the royal house of Damnonia; the great monasteries of Menevia (St. David's), Bangor, Iscoed, Llancarfan, and Llantwit, which influenced British monasticism so much, are all traceable to its influence. It is probable also, notwithstanding the legends of St. Joseph of Arimathaea, that Glastonbury owed its real origin to Irish monks, though whether to Brychan or directly to St. Patrick, as has been alleged, is not certainly known. The missions to Cornwall were both Irish and Irish-Welsh. The earliest directly Irish mission is held by some to have been that led by St. Kiaran, known in the west country as St. Piran, who seems to have arrived in Cornwall about A.D. 490, and established his first hermitage near Perranporth, where the ruined oratory of St. Piran now stands (p. 64). Missions more important through the large following which accompanied the leaders were those of St. Fingar, or Gwinear, and St. Ia, who at the beginning of the sixth century landed in north Cornwall, where their names are perpetuated in those of Gwinear and St. Ives: Gwinear had already been in Brittany, where he had established settlements among the British refugees from the Saxon invasion now rapidly occupying that country (see above). There were henceforward close relations between the Breton Church and that of Britain, of which it was practically a part. The monastic institutions founded by Irish saints in Wales and Cornwall sent out further settlements: Welshmen from Menevia (St. David's), Llantwit Major and Llancarfan, from the monasteries of St. David, St. Illtyd, and St. Cadoc, founded settlements in east and north-east Cornwall; among their number were certainly St. Petroc and St. Sampson, perhaps even St. David and St. Cadoc in person. Bretons came over from Brittany to the country about the Lizard, and by the end of the sixth century Cornwall was filled with Celtic monasteries.

In Scotland the conditions encountered by the Irish missions differed from those of countries farther south. The northern Picts were still pagans, for the colony of Irish Scots of Dalriada had not yet moved northwards to Argyll. Strathclyde, the region between the two Roman walls, stretching from the Clyde to the Derwent in Cumberland, formed part of the British Church, and from about the middle of the sixth century witnessed the labours of St. Kentigern or Mungo. It was not until the year A.D. 563 that Columba, born in Donegal in A.D. 521, founded his monastery on the island of Iona (Hy) to the west of Mull, and began preaching to the Picts. In A.D. 574 Aidan became a member of Columba's community, and after a long sojourn in Iona set out in A.D. 635 to evangelize Northumbria. Here King Oswald, himself at an earlier date a refugee in Iona, befriended him, and he became bishop of Lindisfarne or Holy Island. Lindisfarne now became a great centre of monastic influence, and among the names connected with it are those of Ceadda (Chad), a disciple of Aidan, afterwards bishop of the Mercians (d. A.D. 672), and of Cuthbert, another bishop of Lindisfarne (d. A.D. 687). Until the Danish invasions compelled its removal, the monastery stood for the Celtic usage against the Roman; the latter, introduced by Augustine in A.D. 597, found its chief advocate in the north in Wilfrid of Hexham. As a result of the missions emanating from Ireland, the Irish monastic spirit now permeated the British lands from the Clyde to Brittany. The effort of these Celtic missions, reacting from the extreme west of the continent, did not stop in western Britain and Northumbria. In the period between the sixth and the eighth centuries it penetrated northern France, Switzerland, South Germany, and North and South Italy, taking with it a Celtic art which has left its mark in the illuminations of many manuscripts painted in the above-named countries. The movement only ceased when the Rule of St. Benedict proved too strong for the less highly organized Celtic system.

Two points should be remembered with regard to this return of Christianity from the west of the continent. The first is that it represented the more ascetic faith of the old Gallic monasteries whence St. Patrick originally brought it. The second is that this monastic Christianity was precisely that in which oriental influence was strongest. Monasticism never forgot that it originated in the East; and personal relations between the Houses of the East and West, frequent in the early centuries, continued down to much later times. This is one reason why we find in the decoration of Celtic MSS. and sculptured stones so many analogies to the ornament of Coptic Egypt and of Hither Asia.

This changed and reanimated Church confronted the successors of St. Augustine and the supporters of Rome in the north, like St. Wilfrid, when the Roman mission, once firmly established in the first years of the seventh century, sought to bring the Celtic usage into conformity with that of Rome. Had the Irish missions never taken place, had the Church in Britain remained as it was in the fifth century, the difficulties which even the Synod of Whitby (A.D. 664) did not wholly overcome might never have arisen. As it was, the branches of the Celtic Church conformed only by slow degrees on the principal point in dispute, the keeping of Easter: South Ireland acquiesced in A.D. 626-8; North Ireland in A.D. 692; Northumbria (Anglian, but converted by Celts), in A.D. 664; East Devon and Somerset, comprising the Celts in the King-

dom of Wessex in A.D. 705, the Southern Picts in A.D. 710;
the Scots of Dalriada, and the Picts under the influence of
Iona in A. D. 716–18; Strathclyde in A. D. 721; North Wales in
A.D. 768; South Wales in A. D. 777; Cornwall in the main about
A. D. 850, though perhaps not completely until the early years
of the tenth century. It is held by good authorities that
the high crosses of Ruthwell and Bewcastle (p. 66) were
probably erected in the last quarter of the seventh century,
to commemorate the achievement of the Synod of Whitby. In
estimating the eastern influences affecting earlier Christian
art in Britain, we must not forget that both Augustine and
Theodore came to England from an orientalized Rome
(p. 45).

Early Christian remains in Britain. The oldest church of
which traces have been discovered is that at Silchester, already

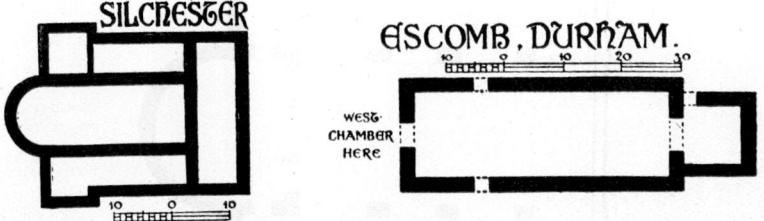

FIG. 35. Fourth-century basilica at Silchester. Church of Celtic plan at
Escomb. (*Archaeological Journal*, liii, 1896.)

mentioned (p. 56), excavated by the Society of Antiquaries
of London in 1892. The remains consist of the foundations
of a fourth-century basilica, and show that the building has
a nave and two aisles, a single apse at the west end, and
a porch or narthex across the east end. the orientation of the
building not conforming to the usage which later became
general. The total length of the nave was only thirty feet;
the aisles, five feet in breadth, ended towards the west in
rather wider chambers or quasi-transepts which appear to
have been walled across, suggesting the *prothesis* and *diakonikon* (p. 97 and fig. 35). Presumably the aisles were divided
from the nave by columns or piers in the manner of the
Graeco-Roman basilicas. The type is thought to have affinities
in the east Mediterranean area. No complete foundations of
any other church dating from the time of the Roman occupation are at present known to exist; of the stone church

built by Ninian at Whitherne (Whithorn) in Galloway no remains survive sufficient to indicate its plan. Part of St. Martin's at Canterbury, the chancel rather than the nave, may have belonged to a Romano-British church restored for Queen Bertha before the coming of Augustine (A. D. 597); the rest of the church dates from the seventh century. Romano-British churches may also have stood on the sites of Brixworth and Reculver (see below), though no traces of them are visible. The church in the castle of Dover is post-Roman, but the bell-tower at its west end is the ancient Roman lighthouse, or *pharos*, converted to a new use. The nature of the primitive

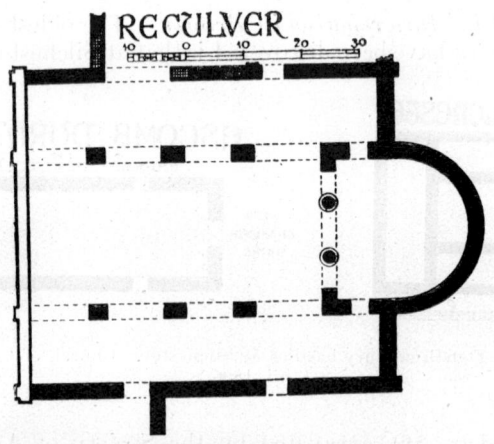

FIG. 36.—Seventh-century basilica, Reculver. (*Archaeological Journal*, liii, 1896.)

churches, which must have been erected after the withdrawal of the Romans, is best known to us from remains of later buildings erected by the Irish immigrants. The type was simple, beginning from a rude hut with an altar at the east side and a small door at the west; to this a larger chamber was added on the western side to shelter the worshippers, and the communicating door only grew by degrees into a small arch. In its later development, the Celtic church consisted of a small square-ended presbytery opening by a narrow arch into a somewhat larger nave without aisles.

The Graeco-Roman basilican form, with central nave divided from the aisle by columns, was re-introduced from

Rome by St. Augustine at the end of the sixth century;
the first church of this kind built for him was his cathedral
at Canterbury, of which nothing now remains. Some of
the oldest churches erected by the Roman mission of which
parts still survive are of small size, without aisles, though
with apses in the Italian fashion. These are six in number:
St. Pancras and St. Martin at Canterbury; Lyminge and
Rochester in Kent; St. Peter-on-the-Wall, Bradwell, Essex;
and South Elmham, Suffolk. None of these churches was
built later than the seventh century, and more than one may
go back to the last years of the sixth; St. Martin's at

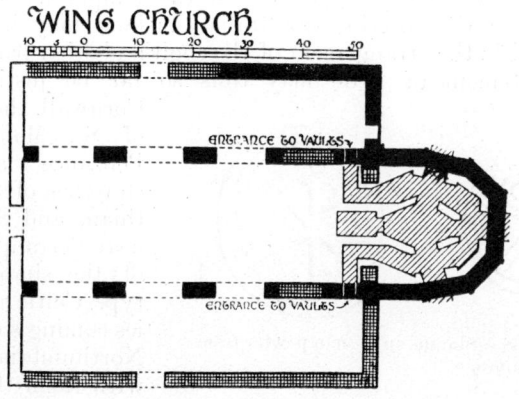

FIG. 37.—Seventh-century basilica, Wing. (*Archaeological Journal*, liii, 1896.)

Canterbury has been already mentioned as probably having
a chancel of Roman date. Other early basilicas of the Italian
type were built at Reculver, Kent (fig. 36), where only the
foundations remain; Brixworth in Northamptonshire, where
the aisles are gone and the apse has been restored; Peter-
borough, where foundations of a basilica exist within the
cathedral; Hexham, Northumberland, and Ripon, Yorks, in
each of which the crypt represents part of the original
basilican church erected by St. Wilfrid; York, where foundations of a basilica were discovered within the minster; and
Wing, Buckinghamshire (fig. 37), still possessing a very perfect
presbytery and vaults, and some original walling of aisles
and clerestory. All these churches date from the seventh
century, those of Wing and Brixworth retaining more of the

original work than the rest. The missionary period inaugurated by St. Augustine lasted for about a century from A.D. 597, the fusion of the Celtic and Roman elements not being completed until many years after the Synod of Whitby in A.D. 664; at the close of the missionary period, no more basilican churches were built on the Italian plan. Though Bede says that Benedict Biscop's churches at Monkwearmouth and Jarrow were influenced by the Italian type, the remains of the original work in both places reveal the Celtic single-chamber plan, and not the basilican, as in the case of Wilfrid's contemporary churches at Hexham; a third church at Escomb, Durham (fig. 35), is of the same age and type. In all three the Celtic influence is shown in the simple narrow plan, though in the interior the Italian fashion may have been followed in the arrangement of the choir and other particulars; the statement of Bede may thus so far be justified. In Cornwall, the oratory of St. Maddern at Penzance, and the churches of St. Gwythian, and St. Piran near Perranporth, are of the simple Celtic type. Celtic missionaries coming south from Northumbria brought with them their narrow, aisleless form of church. This 'met and was modified by the Italian form, but contributed the larger share to the shaping of the English tradition. Most small English churches are built on a plan which is purely Scottish (Irish) all through the Saxon time and beyond it.' (Micklethwaite.)

Fig. 38.—Stamps on Roman pewter from the Thames.

Lesser monuments of Romano-British Christianity are not very common, and it may be of interest to mention some of those now preserved, or known to have existed in comparatively recent times. A Christian tombstone of the Romano-British period inscribed with a Latin name was found not long ago in use as a gate-post between Parracombe and Lynton in Devonshire. Another tombstone, also with a Latin inscription, and known as the Carnsew stone, is at Hayle in Cornwall. The floor-mosaic of a Roman villa at Frampton in Dorsetshire has the sacred monogram in its earlier form. A tile from the corridor steps of another villa at Chedworth in Gloucestershire is also engraved with the monogram, which is further found

PLATE V. BYZANTINE IVORY PANEL: THE DEATH OF JACOB.
(See p. 169.)

upon crosses and inscribed stones in Galloway, Wales, and Cornwall (at least six examples), and one example occurs at Kirk Maughold in the Isle of Man. Authorities are not agreed whether all these stones date from the period of the Roman occupation, but the apparent absence of the monogram in Ireland is in favour of an early date for those in Britain on which it occurs. The Galloway stones, five in number, are on two peninsulas, on one of which, called the Machers, stood St. Ninian's stone church, known as *Candida casa*, or white house. Where the sacred monogram occurs, it is of the second or upright form (⳨), and there seems good reason to believe that they date approximately from the time of Ninian. The stone at Penmachno in North Wales has a ⳨ with a Latin inscription to one Carausius, showing that it surmounted a cairn of stones above the grave; it should also date from the fifth century. A stone at St. Just in Cornwall, with a similar upright monogram, suggests a like period.

Mosaic pavements of Roman date from Thruxton, Hants (in the British Museum, North East Staircase), and Horkstow, Yorkshire, have in their designs crosses by many considered to indicate a Christian origin, for though the cross as a Christian symbol is generally later than the time of the Roman occupation, this is not a universal rule (p. 80). The cross on the lid of the third-century sarcophagus of the Roman Valerius Amandinus, at the entrance to the Chapter House at Westminster Abbey, seems to be mediaeval, though it has some affinities to work of the fifth and sixth centuries.

Various smaller objects in Great Britain, dating from the time of the Roman occupation, bear marks of Christian origin, though it should be noted that they need not all have been made in the country. The fine silver treasure found in 1919 at Traprain Law in East Lothian, perhaps the hidden spoil of barbarian raiders, contains several objects dating from about the end of the fourth century in which the monogram in its earlier form is seen; one is a silver flask which bears an inscription, another a spoon, the third a *colatorium* or strainer for the consecrated wine (see p. 111). A fourth object in the Traprain treasure, a silver flagon, has reliefs representing Adam and Eve, Moses striking the rock, and the Adoration of the Magi. Two finger rings from Fifehead Neville, Dorsetshire; terra-cotta lamps, one in the Museum at Newcastle-on-Tyne; a vase of Caistor ware at Alnwick Castle; a lead seal or stamp from Silchester, now in the Reading Museum—all bear the sacred monogram. A silver vessel found at Corbridge in

Northumberland, engraved with the same symbol, is now unfortunately lost. In the British Museum Room of Roman Britain, Table-Case A, are cakes of pewter stamped with the monogram, found in the Thames at Battersea (fig. 38), and in Wall-Case 47 a dish, part of a pewter service, found on the site of the Roman villa at Appleshaw, Hants : in this service the fish-shaped dish, itself engraved with a fish, and the chalice-like cup should also be noted. Other minor objects of the period of the Roman occupation without monogram or cross, but almost certainly Christian, may be mentioned. A gold ring from Brancaster in Norfolk has the acclamation: *vivas in Deo,* 'live in God'. A ring from Silchester, in the Reading Museum, has the same inscription as that from Brancaster; a fragment of a glass vessel in the same place and from the same site is engraved with a fish and a palm-branch; the Reading Museum also possesses a Gnostic gem excavated at Silchester. The Dorchester Museum has a collection of Roman spoons found with coins dating from A.D. 360 to about A.D. 400; one of these has a fish rudely engraved in the bowl, another the inscription : AVGVSTINI VIVAS. In view of the other Christian objects of Roman date from the same county mentioned above (Frampton, Fifehead Neville) these spoons may be regarded as having probably belonged to a Romano-British Christian, though they may have been made in the North of France. Other spoons with similar acclamations have been found in England.

Christian art in the Anglo-Saxon period is first represented in Anglian monuments of Northumbria and upon its borders dating from the latter part of the seventh century. The most famous of these are the two high crosses at Ruthwell in Dumfries and Bewcastle in Cumberland, mentioned above (p. 61). The fine tradition manifest in the figure-subjects suggests an immigrant art, and the models may have been ivory carvings of East-Christian origin brought from Rome by such men as Benedict Biscop and St. Wilfrid (p. 64), the former of whom visited Rome five times to obtain vestments, books, pictures, and other objects for the enrichment of his churches. These prelates are said to have imported masons from Gaul, some of whom may have been carvers in stone. A number of other reliefs in the Northumbrian region illustrate the persistence of this glyptic art, and suggest that foreign example soon awakened a native talent of no mean order; thus the upright slabs of Scotland show a vigorous figure sculpture practised in the eighth century and later. Very interesting remains from the sites of the earliest northern monasteries are the small, almost square stone slabs often called 'pillow-stones' because an unauthenticated early account of the discovery at Hartlepool states that they were placed beneath the heads of skeletons. These stones bear incised crosses, with inscriptions both in runes and Roman character, and belong to interments of monks and nuns in the late seventh or the eighth century. Examples from the monastery of Hartlepool, founded in A.D. 640 and probably destroyed by the Danes about A.D. 800, are exhibited in the

Fig. 39.—Silver chalice of the time of Alfred, from Trewhiddle, Cornwall.

adjoining Iron Age Gallery (Wall-Case 35). Other examples have been found at Lindisfarne, Wensley, Billingham, and Birtley; similar stones occur in Ireland (Clonmacnois, Monasterboice). The wooden coffin of St. Cuthbert (*d*. 687), dating from the close of the seventh century, and preserved in the Chapter Library at Durham, is ornamented with incised figures of Our Lord, the Virgin and Child, apostles, angels, and Evangelists' symbols.

Northumbrian Christianity is further illustrated by smaller works of art very little later than the crosses, two of which, the Franks Casket (No. 30, *Catalogue of Ivory Carvings*) and the Lindisfarne Gospels, or Durham Book, are in the British Museum, the former in the collection of Anglo-Saxon antiquities (Iron Age Gallery, in a special case), the latter in the Department Manuscripts. The casket, which is ascribed to about A.D. 700, is made of whale's bone, and carved with runic inscriptions, historical and religious subjects (Romulus and Remus, the Taking of Jerusalem, the Adoration of the Magi), and scenes derived from northern mythology. It has no Celtic features, and the nature of the historical subjects suggests that it may have been partly inspired by some early illuminated Chronicle of the type first produced for Theophilus, patriarch of Alexandria, who died in A.D. 412.

The Lindisfarne Gospels were written by Eadfrith bishop of Lindisfarne (A.D. 698–721) in honour of St. Cuthbert. The book is illuminated in the Irish manner introduced into Northumbria from Iona, but contains four full-page portraits of the Evangelists seated at their desks as depicted in the Christian East, the earliest known example of the type being in the Gospel at Rossano (p. 122). These portraits are accompanied by their names in the Greek form, but written in Latin letters (e.g. *O agius Marcus*, for ὁ ἅγιος Μάρκος). The method in these figure-subjects is more naturalistic than in the case of purely Irish MSS. of the eight or ninth century, like the Gospels of St. Chad at Lichfield or the famous Book of Kells, where the figures are treated primarily as decoration. The most characteristic work in the book, the ornament, is predominantly Celtic, and the style which it represents has been described as Hiberno-Saxon.

Anglo-Saxon antiquities with Christian subjects or symbols from the Midlands and the South of England may be seen in the Iron Age Gallery. They include the stoup from a grave at Long Wittenham, Berkshire, with the sacred monogram, the Annunciation, Baptism, and Miracle of Cana (Wall-Case 38); the gold rings of King Ethelwulf (A.D. 837–57), with confronted peacocks on a niello ground, and Ethelswith, Queen of Mercia (A.D. 855–9), with the *Agnus Dei* (Table-Case D); a cruciform pendant with coin of Heraclius (A.D. 610–641), found at Wilton, Norfolk (Table-Case D, Section 2). A reproduction of the well-known enamelled ornament in the Ashmolean Museum at Oxford, known as the Alfred Jewel, is exhibited in Table-Case D. A plain silver chalice, of the time of Alfred (fig. 39), found in A.D. 1774 at Trewhiddle, near St. Austell in Cornwall, is also shown in the Iron Age Gallery (Wall-Case 52).

II. The Catacombs, and Early Christian Iconography.

a. *The Catacombs.*

The earliest traditions of Christian art are associated with the subterranean burial-places called catacombs. Different origins have been suggested for this curious name. One view is that it is derived from two Greek words κατά and κύμβη meaning 'at or near the hollow or valley', and that it was first applied to a district near the Appian Way, probably owing to the configuration of the ground; another derives it from the same Greek word κατά and the late Latin *accubitorium*, a tomb. It originally referred to the Christian cemeteries excavated on a certain section of the Appian Way; then it was restricted to one of these, that of St. Sebastian; finally it came to be used as a general term for all similar places of burial wherever situated. The word used by the Early Christians themselves was not catacomb, but cemetery (*coemeterium*), the Latin version of the Greek κοιμητήριον or sleeping-place.

The Roman catacombs were not beneath the city, but, like the pagan tombs, beyond it, along the great highways running from the capital to various parts of Italy; Roman law forbade interment within the city walls. The *tufa*, forming the subsoil near Rome, is peculiarly adapted to the excavation of underground galleries, and this circumstance proved very favourable to the early Christians, who naturally followed the oriental custom of burial in subterranean chambers instead of burning their dead. The need for concealment and the desire to protect the graves of the departed from profanation were, therefore, not the reasons which led to the formation of underground cemeteries, although in times of persecution their dark recesses were naturally adopted as places of refuge.

It was not until the second half of the first century that the Christians adopted the system of collective burial on a large scale. They had previously either shared the Jewish catacombs already existing near the capital, or had been buried in small *hypogea* or crypts united by short passages. But when once the practice had begun, it spread with great rapidity, and no less than fifty catacombs are now known to exist, the earliest of which dates from the period named. The first large cemeteries were probably extensions of the tombs of wealthy Christian families, such as that of the Flavii, which had a legal title to certain plots of land for sepulchral purposes. These families, which lent their houses for the services of the Church, in like manner opened their places of burial to other members of the congregation, and from these the greater catacombs were developed. At first

Fig. 40.—*Loculi* in the Catacombs (after Perret).

all cemeteries were thus held by private tenure; but by the time of the persecutions, the Church, as represented by her bishops, had entered into collective possession, and was recognized as owner by the imperial authorities. Whether her rights were secured through a legal fiction by which Christian communities registered themselves as burial societies after the fashion of similar pagan institutions, or whether they were enjoyed simply by toleration, is a point on which differences of opinion exist. Every burial site included a certain superficial space (*area*) often enclosed by a hedge or wall and planted with cypresses, in which were built small *cellae* or memorial chapels, and where sarcophagi might be placed. Here too the dead were from quite an early period interred in graves dug from the surface of the ground, as many as ten bodies being sometimes laid one above the other but each separated from the next by a slab of stone. Surface interment

Fig. 41.—A chamber in the Roman Catacombs (after De Rossi).

was practised concurrently with catacomb burial, and by the fifth century had quite superseded it.

The catacombs were systems of corridors and small chambers partially lighted by shafts (*luminaria*) which opened on the surface of the soil, and were sometimes cut in several tiers or storeys, one below the other. As they were frequently excavated in rising ground, the entrances were often in the sides of the hills and were approached through a kind of antechamber or vestibule. Except in the neighbourhood of the shafts, or near the entrances, artificial light was always necessary, and this was provided by lamps similar in general character to those seen in the collection (Wall-Cases 7, 8 and 11, 12; figs. 10 and 20). Along the sides of the vaulted corridors, which were from two to four feet wide and little more than the height of a man, were cut horizontal rectangular niches (*loculi*) one above the other, in which bodies were laid, the opening at the front being closed by slabs of marble or tiles, on which inscriptions were engraved (fig. 40). In the chambers (*cubicula*) similar tombs were arranged around the sides, and there were also recessed tombs opening at the top, the most characteristic of which, the so-called *arcosolia*, had a rounded arch above them. Figure 41 provides illustrations of both these kinds of tombs. Stone sarcophagi were also placed in the niches, but these were not common during the first three centuries.

Although most of the *cubicula* were family vaults, some crypts were apparently constructed for religious services. One of these, dating from the third century, presents many of the features of the later *basilicas* (see p. 91), such as the apse and *presbyterium* with the episcopal chair; but sometimes the place of the apse is taken by an *arcosolium* tomb, the top of which was evidently used as an altar. These catacomb chapels were probably used for funeral and memorial services, especially in the fourth century when the cult of the martyrs became general, but they were not adapted for regular public worship; for this they were too small, as few of them could accommodate more than fifty people. The earliest inscriptions of the catacombs are of a very simple character, merely giving the barest details, with perhaps a pious formula such as *vivas in Deo, pax tecum*. Many of them are in Greek, which was for a long time the language of the Church, but these cease with the fourth century. As time went on, more elaborate inscriptions are found and new formulae were introduced, but as a general rule we learn little more than the name and age of the deceased, the day of his death and the relationship borne to him by the persons who caused the inscription to be set up. The age is often given with great precision in years, months, and days, though after the third century there is often a greater vagueness, and we meet with such statements as 'who lived about twenty-five years'; the simplest early Christian symbols often accompany the inscriptions (fig. 40), but sometimes symbolical scriptural scenes such as the Raising of Lazarus occur. It

may be noted here that the custom of dating by the year of
Our Lord did not exist at the earliest period of Christianity;
it first arose in the sixth century, but examples are rare
before the eighth. Tombs were generally dated by mention
of the consuls' names, which are found down to the abolition
of the consulate in the time of Justinian; but after the
peace of the Church the names of popes are occasionally
given. Other means of dating were by eras, such as that
of the foundation of Rome, or that of Diocletian, beginning
A.D. 284; or again, at a later period, by *indictions*, which
were periods of fifteen years at the end of which taxa-
tion was revised. In very early times Christians had three
names, like the ancient Romans, but this custom was soon
dropped, and by the end of the fourth century only one name

Fig. 42.—Inscription from the Catacombs (after Marucchi).

was usual. About the same time eulogistic epithets and
phrases directly indicating the belief of the deceased were
introduced, and details were added with regard to his station
in life. With the fourth century, too, mistakes in orthography
became common, and we perceive the first signs of the
transition between the old Latin and mediaeval and modern
Italian. The word most generally used for burial by the early
Christians was *depositio*; the familiar formula *hic jacet* begins
with the fifth century. Common formulae were very frequently
abbreviated, IN P or I. P. standing for *in pace*, and S. T. T. L.
for *sit tibi terra levis*, 'may the earth rest lightly upon
thee!' Many tombs in the catacombs had no name inscribed
upon them, but were simply identified by small objects impressed
in the mortar which fixed the slabs of the *loculi* in their places
at the time of the interment. The finest inscriptions of
the catacombs are those made by order of Pope Damasus at

the close of the fourth century to mark the tombs of the martyrs; they are generally metrical panegyrics engraved on marble slabs in very beautiful characters.

Nearly all of the catacombs were decorated with mural painting, for which the stucco walls and roofs of the chambers afforded an ample field. The style, introduced from Alexandria, is that of contemporary pagan art adapted to new conditions and modified in accordance with Christian ideas. The earlier work recalls the graceful frescoes of Pompeii; but after the second century there is a falling-off in execution.

When the attainment of sole power by the Emperor Constantine the Great had made Christianity the official religion of

Fig. 43.—Front of a stone sarcophagus from France (after Le Blant).

the cosmopolitan Roman Empire, the practice of burying in catacombs began to decline, and interments now generally took place in superficial cemeteries, where large churches were now built. It was at this time that sculptured stone sarcophagi (figs. 43 and 52) were produced in large numbers, for wealthy Christians had become numerous, and distinctively Christian subjects could be openly executed in sculptors' workshops without the risk of interference. The multiplication of these sarcophagi, which have been found not only in Italy but also in France, Spain, and other countries, was of great importance to the development of Christian figure sculpture down to the time of the barbarian invasions. Inscribed tombstones like those seen in Wall-Cases 14 and 15, which have been found in large numbers in provincial cemeteries, especially on the Rhine, in

France, Spain, and N. Africa, also became common in this period. The earlier inscriptions are simple in character and resemble those of the catacombs, but the formulae used vary with different localities; the majority date from the fourth to the seventh century, but in Spain examples in this style are known as late as the close of the eighth. In spite of the change which Constantine's conversion made in the position of Christianity, catacomb burial still remained fairly general until about A.D. 350, and did not fall into disuse until the first quarter of the fifth century. At that time the incursions of the Goths and Vandals began to make the outside country unsafe, and during the siege of Rome by the Gothic king Alaric (A. D. 410) the first cemetery within the walls was laid out near the baths of Diocletian. About a century and a half later interment within the city walls became the rule, for owing to the great depopulation of the city the enforcement of the old law was no longer necessary. Down to the time of the Lombard invasions the bodies of the martyrs mostly remained in the catacombs, and their tombs were the objects of frequent pilgrimages, especially in the seventh century; but in the eighth and ninth centuries their remains were removed for security to the churches within the city. During the Middle Ages the knowledge of the catacombs was gradually lost, and by the fifteenth century that beneath the church of Saint Sebastian was almost the only one still accessible to the pilgrims who came to Rome from the various countries of Europe. So matters continued until the end of the sixteenth century, when the accidental falling in of a vault in a vineyard, by laying bare the frescoes with which the walls were decorated, excited public curiosity in these long-forgotten places of burial. Antonio Bosio (*d.* A. D. 1629), 'the Columbus of the Catacombs', made the first extensive and systematic excavations, and since his death each century witnessed the publication of important books on underground Rome; the best idea of the mural paintings may be gained from the great work of Wilpert.

The Roman Catacombs are naturally the most famous; but large underground burial-places of the same kind were created in other places. The catacombs of St. Januarius (St. Gennaro) and other saints at Naples, those of St. Giovanni near Syracuse, and those at Malta are important western examples. In North Africa, those of Alexandria are decorated in a manner similar to those of Rome, as was to be expected from the very close relationship between the art of the two cities. Other catacombs in North Africa are found at Cyrene, and further west in Tunis (the former Proconsular Province), where those of Hadrumetum or Susa (Sousse) have yielded interesting remains of the Early Christian centuries (cf. p. 176). In the Holy Land there are catacombs in the north part of the Mount of Olives, where both Christian and Jewish interments have been found; the use of rock-cut tombs was customary among the Jews and other peoples of Asia, whose practice the Christians followed. Burial chambers cut in the rock are recorded from Syria, Mesopotamia, and Asia Minor.

b. *Early Christian Iconography.*

The term iconography is derived from two Greek words, literally meaning the description of images or figures. For the archaeologist it means the expression in art of persons, events, and even ideas, and the analysis and comparison of the types expressed: broadly speaking, it represents subject-matter as opposed to style. Where large numbers of instances are compared and analysed, iconography may be expanded to very wide limits; the present section can only offer a few elementary notes on points of particular or general interest.

During the first three centuries, when Christianity was not officially tolerated within the Roman Empire, the indirect presentation of ideas by means of symbols was imposed by circumstances upon the artist, and there was no scope for a historical art. Even when persons were introduced, as distinguished from allegorical figures or characters, individuality was not attempted, but ideal or generalized types sufficed. A few of the oldest of all Christian symbols may first be mentioned.

The Fish. This type, perhaps first introduced from Alexandria, was among the earliest symbols of the Saviour, for the Greek name Ἰχθύς gave rise to an acrostic which was known as early as the second century, the five component letters standing for the initials of the five words Ἰησοῦς Χριστός Θεοῦ Υἱός Σωτήρ, *Jesus Christ, Son of God, Saviour.* As the dolphin is frequently used with this meaning, it has been suggested that the fish was first adopted on account of the old classical traditions of the dolphin as the friend of man and the rescuer of shipwrecked mariners, but the earliest representations show us another kind of fish more like that seen in figs. 44 and 46. In rarer and later examples fish stand for the faithful, and the fisherman for Christ. The symbolic fish is found upon early Celtic and Teutonic monuments in Britain and France.

The Ship is the symbol of the Church in which the faithful are borne safely over the sea of life to the haven of

Fig. 44.—Engraved gem: fish, crook, and palm-branch. (No. 35.)

Fig. 45.—Engraved gem : a ship. (No. 40.)

Fig. 46.—Engraved gem: anchor, fish, and dove. (No. 3.)

Fig. 47.—Engraved gem : anchor, doves, palm-branch, and fishes. (No. 39.)

Fig. 48.—Engraved gem: the Good Shepherd. (No. 2.)

eternity (fig. 45); sometimes rowers and steersman are visible, but at others only the oars are seen. Occasionally it is accompanied by other symbols such as the dolphin or the sacred monogram.

The Anchor (figs. 46 and 47) symbolizes hope, and sometimes rests upon a fish, to indicate that the Christian's hope is based on Christ.

The Good Shepherd (fig. 48). The figure of a shepherd

carrying a lamb over his shoulders and a crook in his hand was of obvious application to Christianity. It recalled the passages in the Gospels (John x. 1–27; Matt. xv. 24; Luke xv. 4–5; John xxi. 15–17), and was perhaps also considered to symbolize Christ as the leader of souls in their passage to the other world. Some have conjectured that the motive of the Good Shepherd was borrowed from the common pagan type of Hermes (Mercury) carrying a ram, but this view has not found general acceptance. The Good Shepherd usually holds a staff or crook (*pedum*) in his hand, and this is sometimes used as a symbol by itself, as also are the lambs representing his flock, one or two of which are usually seen at his feet. In the fourth century first occur representations of the lamb as symbol of the Redeemer, while on the Roman mosaics sheep are often used to represent the disciples.

Fig. 48ᵃ.—Engraved gem: dove on fish, with olive-branch and sacred monogram. (No. 6.)

The Dove usually stands for the soul of the departed, and often bears in its beak the olive branch, itself the symbol of peace, in allusion to the history of the ark (fig. 48ᵃ).

The Palm-branch is the emblem of Victory, as in the pagan world.

The above are the oldest and most authentic symbols found on the monuments. Those which follow were of less universal acceptation and held to be rather later in date. Such of them as represent animals, either real or fabulous, had probably long been known to popular tradition in the East, where the attribution of moral and mystical qualities to beasts was very general. Not long after the beginning of our era, and probably at Alexandria, these traditions were embodied in a work called the *Physiologus* or book of Natural History, from which similar books called Bestiaries, so popular in the Middle Ages, were in later times derived. From the large number of these symbols, the following may be selected: the *serpent*, generally typifying the Evil One; the *peacock*, immortality, either from the fact that it sheds and renews its tail-feathers every year, or on account of an old tradition that its flesh was incorruptible; the fabulous *phoenix*, reborn from its own ashes, the Resurrection; and the *stag*, the soul thirsting for the water of baptism; the stag is often represented as drinking from a fountain or a vase, as on mosaics from Carthage on the wall of the North West Staircase, to which a Christian origin is attributed (fig. 49). Among other popular symbols, the *tree*, especially the palm-tree when used as an accessory, indicated that the scene represents Paradise; the *vine*, though often purely decorative, has occasionally a reference to the Eucharist; the *triangle*, which has been found with the palm and a form of the sacred monogram, appears to indicate the Trinity.

A few words must now be said on the subject of the sacred monogram ☧, to which allusion has just been made. It is formed from *Chi* and *Rho* the first two letters of the Greek word

Fig. 49.—Harts drinking from fountain; mosaic from Carthage in the British Museum; sixth century.

Χριστός (Christ = the anointed), and is therefore often called the *Chi-Rho*; Eusebius (d. about A.D. 340) relates in his Life of Constantine that by command of that emperor it was placed in a wreath at the top of the imperial standard or *labarum* (fig. 50). It had various forms at different periods, some of which are identical with monograms on coins struck before the birth of Christ; one of these (⯁) is used as an abbreviation for the word τρίχαλκον upon coins of Herod I (B.C. 37–B.C. 4). Another, of later date, (☧), stands for the word ἄρχοντος on Phrygian and Lydian coins of the time of the early Roman emperors. The use of such monograms as abridgements of words upon coins was commonest about the period of Septimius Severus (A.D. 193–211), and was thus long anterior to Constantine. For Christian inscriptions, the *Chi-Rho*, in the so-called Constantinian form, was similarly used as an abbreviation of the name of Christ in the catacombs as early as the second century, *IN* ☧, for example, standing for *in Christo*. Its independent use as an actual symbol of Our Lord is not proved before the time of Constantine, but it becomes common in the second quarter of the fourth century, at the close of which it is often flanked by α and ω (*alpha* and *omega*), the first and last letters of the Greek alphabet, in allusion to Rev. i. 8, 11; xxi. 6; xxii. 13. About the middle of that century, however, a new form was introduced by the addition of a horizontal line, and this perhaps formed a transition to the so-called monogrammatic cross (☧) which first became common after A.D. 355, and continued through part of the following century (cf. the lamp, fig. 11). Another view as to the origin of the monogrammatical cross is that it is a combination of the T-cross and the letter P. The form had appeared in isolated cases as early as the reign of Constantine.

The Cross. The general use of the cross as a Christian symbol is later than that of the monogram. On certain early monuments it is thought to have been represented in a veiled manner, as by the crossyard of a mast (cf. Fig. 45) or by the cross-bar of an anchor (Fig. 47), but in the catacombs at any rate it appears without disguise in inscriptions of the second century, appearing also on coins of Constantine, and on monuments of the fourth century. The *tau*, so called from the Greek character T, the St. Andrew's cross (derived at some time from the Latin numeral ten (X = *decussis*, whence *crux decussata*)), and the

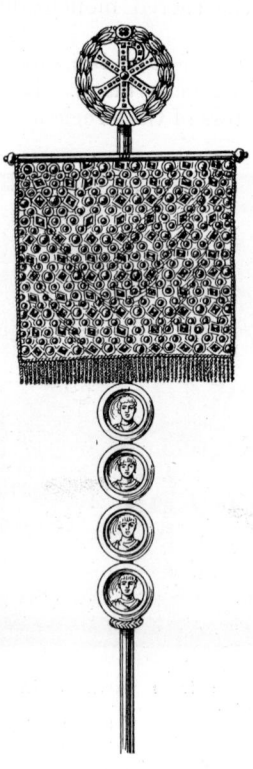

FIG. 50.—Reconstruction of the *labarum* (after J. Wilpert, Die römischen Mosaiken und Malereien, 1916).

PLATE VI.—SILVER BRIDAL CASKET OF PROJECTA.
(*See* p. 174.)

Latin cross with long lower limb, are all found as early as the second century, and it is shown below that on gems even the Crucifixion appears at a similar early date (p. 84). But its open and common employment came in with the fifth century. At the very beginning of this century it is seen on the ivory panels in the Museum collection (pl. II) where Our Lord is seen bearing a cross with long shaft, and crucified upon the same. The swastika (卍), a very ancient symbol common to Early Greek and Buddhist art and found upon prehistoric objects in Europe, occurs in the Roman Catacombs, but was never widely adopted; it is to be seen on some of the Celtic pillar-stones in Scotland and Ireland. The use of the old Egyptian hieroglyph *ankh* (☥) to represent the cross was confined to the Copts of Egypt. The sacred monogram did not entirely die out on the introduction of the cross, and it is found, for example, on rude stone monuments in Scotland and Wales (see above, p. 65), on seventh-century sarcophagi from Ravenna, and on Byzantine coins and larger monuments of even later date.

Symbols of the Evangelists. The representation of the four Evangelists by means of a winged man, a winged lion, a winged ox, and an eagle is based on the vision of Rev. iv. 6, read in connexion with that of the first chapter of Ezekiel. It is found upon monuments which are claimed for the fourth century, but does not become general until the fifth and sixth. It is characteristic of the West, and is not used in East Christian or Byzantine art until mediaeval times. The application of the symbols to the particular Evangelists was not at first as uniform as it afterwards became.

The orans. This is a male or female figure standing full-face with both arms extended and the palms of the hands raised. The word means 'one who prays'; and this attitude of prayer, which may be remarked upon several objects in the collection (cf. fig. 51), is one of the earliest adopted by the Church. The *orans* generally represents the soul of the departed in Paradise, but is thought to have occasionally symbolized the Church itself.

Symbolical Scenes. In addition to individual objects used as symbols, the Early Christians frequently employed scenes from the Old and New Testaments, and sometimes even from pagan mythology, for a like purpose. Of the latter we may specially mention *Cupid and Psyche*, typifying the purification of the Soul; and Orpheus charming the wild beasts, used as a type of Christ. Cupid and Psyche are represented on a late-

G

Roman sarcophagus in the Museum which some authorities regard as Christian (p. 188 and fig. 52). The Old Testament being prophetic of the New, scenes from the one were treated as complementary to those of the other. Thus Noah in the Ark, Daniel in the lion's den, Isaac led to the altar, Jonah miraculously preserved from death, the Three Children of Babylon in the fiery furnace, and Moses striking the rock, all symbolizing deliverance and redemption by the power of God, are often associated with the raising of Lazarus, the multiplica-

FIG. 51.—Terracotta flask with St. Menas between two camels. (No. 860.)

tion of the loaves, and the Eucharistic feast. These were among the earliest of the scenes depicted by Christian artists, and were followed in the third century by others of a like nature, among which may be mentioned Moses receiving the tables of the Law, the Ascension of Elijah, Susanna between the Elders, and the miracles of Christ, notably the marriage at Cana and the healing of the paralytic or of the blind man.

The nimbus. This Latin word, meaning cloud, was probably in its origin conceived as a luminous cloud issuing from and surrounding the body of a divinity. It is commonly considered to have come from Egypt or the East, and was familiar to the pagan world, not only divinities but personifications of cities being represented with rays surrounding the whole figure or, more commonly, the head alone. Apollo and Mercury were thus glorified, as also were some of the Roman Emperors, while the nimbus is found in the common Christian form of a plain disk on early Buddhist sculptures on the north-west frontier of India (examples are seen in the Buddhist Room, adjoining the Christian Room). Whatever the primary idea of the nimbus may have been, it became the mark of dignity, eminence, or power rather than of sanctity, and with this meaning it is seen on the coins of Christian Emperors, and round the head of the

Fig. 52.—Front of a marble sarcophagus in the British Museum, with Cupid and Psyche: fourth century.

Emperor Justinian in the famous mosaics of St. Vitale at Ravenna; that this was its true significance may be gathered from the arch-mosaics of St. Maria Maggiore, where it is given to Herod. In the West the first authentic instances of the nimbus in Christian art date from the fourth century, and among the earliest are those seen on the gilded glasses, for example on plate XI, where the figure standing behind Daniel, and considered to represent Our Lord, is nimbed. In the fifth century we first find the Virgin Mary and various saints with the nimbus, but for nearly two hundred years its use in the case of saints fluctuated, and it was not general as a sign of sanctity until the sixth century. The nimbus of Our Lord was early distinguished from all others by having a cross described within the circle, and this variety is known as the *cruciferous* (cross-bearing) or, less correctly, cruciform nimbus: in a few instances the sacred monogram is found instead of the cross; the cruciferous nimbus may have been known as early as the close of the third century, but some authorities believe it to be later. The aureole or 'glory' enveloping the whole body, commonly of a pointed-oval shape, and known in the early Middle Ages as the *mandorla* or *vesica piscis* from its supposed resemblance to an almond or to a fish-bladder, is first seen in its completeness in the mosaics of St. Maria Maggiore at Rome (late fourth century).

Before the toleration of Christianity it was the object of the Church to strengthen and encourage the community in the face of persecution, and such events as martyrdom or the Crucifixion were avoided. But it would appear that although the latter subject was usually treated in a symbolic way, as for example on a sarcophagus-fragment in the Lateran, where a veiled T-cross is surmounted by a dove and a phoenix, or on another sarcophagus in the same place, where a cross bears the laurel-wreathed sacred monogram, two soldiers sleeping below, yet in cases where the work was not designed for general view a more realistic treatment is found as early as the second century. The Crucifixion-gem from Constanza on the Black Sea (Table-Case A and fig. 55) affords one instance, and is not the sole example of its kind; it is conjectured that such gems may have been worn or carried secretly for private devotion at a time when larger representations were not to be seen. The well-known derisory *graffito* on the wall of a chamber in the *Domus Gelotiana*, the pages' school in the Imperial Palace on the Palatine Hill at Rome, belongs to a different category; but it shows that the idea of the crucified Christ was familiar in the earlier third century.

When the conversion of Constantine (A. D. 313) led to the toleration of Christianity throughout the Roman Empire the symbolism of early times was no longer necessary, though many of its motives survived as ornament. The Church now required a historical and dogmatic art to celebrate its triumph, set forth the events of sacred story, and illustrate its dogma. These needs gradually changed the whole trend of Christian iconography; and under the Syrian influence now powerful in the monasteries and spreading with their growth, a realistic and dramatic spirit transformed the character of Christian art. This spirit did not shrink from painful details, and it loved to multiply episode and event. Thus from the fifth century the idealizing Hellenistic manner, which gives much of the earliest

Christian representational art so classical a character, was often thrust into the background by a style cruder but more sincere, and more accurately expressing the sentiment of the non-Greek peoples inhabiting the Christian East. From the oriental point of view, no subject connected with the story was regarded as too insignificant or too painful. The events narrated by the Evangelists did not suffice for the vivid eastern fancy, and their number was increased by additions derived from the apocryphal gospels. Throughout the whole period of its history this oriental striving for dramatic expressiveness remained a living force in East Christian art. It was most in evidence in monastic communities in various countries, among which those of Egypt, Syria-Palestine, and Cappadocia played the principal part. Thus Christian art, which had begun with symbolism, became realistic and outspoken, with the result that its iconography was enriched by an influx of new motives. Although Hellenism was never destroyed, it was from the oriental spirit which it now embodied, and from the manner of its expression, that East-Christian religious art derived its distinctive character. On p. 104 something is said of the manner in which subjects were disposed on the walls of churches; the present section may be closed by notes upon a few points of general iconographical interest.

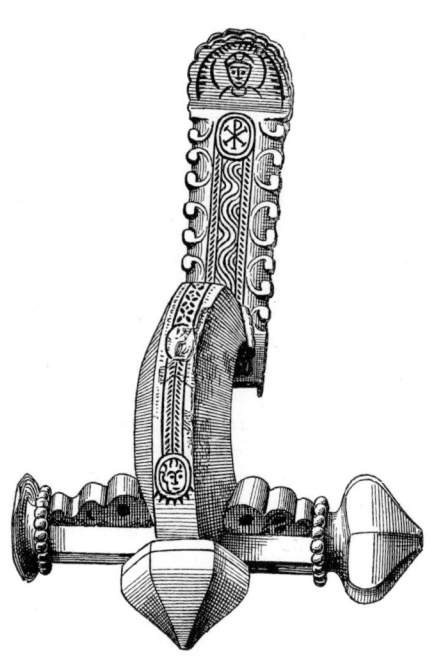

FIG. 53.—Bronze gilt brooch with sacred monogram: fourth century. (No. 256.)

The first concerns the representation of sacred persons who are now characterized and lose their ideal or indefinite quality.

The Portrait of Christ. In the case of Our Lord, the oldest monuments show us what we should expect from the predominance of Hellenistic art during the first centuries, a type based upon a generalized conception of Greek youth. The paintings of the catacombs introduce the gradual development of the adult bearded head which has become consecrated by the usage of centuries. According to Wilpert, the oldest representation as an adult appears in the first half of the second century; the hair, however, still remains short after the Graeco-Roman fashion, and the face is still beardless. The earliest signs of a short beard occur in work dating from the first half of the third century, and this period provides the first instance of the head with short beard, and hair left long in the eastern style. The full beard is not seen until more than a century later, in work of the second half of the fourth century; this type is therefore after the time of Constantine. There is never any fixity of tradition; figures painted by the same hands on the same walls differ essentially from each other. 'This uncertainty sufficiently shows that the painters of the Catacombs were not in possession of a portrait of Christ.' The above points are of interest in connexion with the familiar legends as to contemporary portraits of Our Lord, such as that associated with the name of Abgar King of Edessa. There is no valid evidence that such portraits existed.

The Virgin Mary is generally represented in the catacombs and on the gilded glasses as an *orans*, but, as in the case of Our Lord, there is no attempt at portraiture. The Annunciation scene is thought to occur in a third-century fresco in the catacomb of St. Priscilla, and in the same catacomb is a group held by some to represent the Virgin and Child with the prophet Isaiah; while the Adoration of the Magi also belongs to the art of the catacombs. But though this and the Annunciation are common on the sarcophagi, the wide popularity of portraits of the Virgin did not begin until after the Council of Ephesus in A. D. 431 at which her title as Mother of God was established against the Nestorians (p. 159). It may be added that the Almighty was usually represented in Early Christian art by a hand issuing from a cloud (the so-called *Dextera Dei* or *Dextera Domini*); and this is the manner in which the divine intervention is indicated in such scenes as the Sacrifice of Isaac, the giving of the tables of the law, and the Baptism of Our Lord (plate III). God appears in human form in a few scenes from the Old Testament, for instance when receiving the offerings of Cain and Abel, and giving to Adam and Eve the ears of corn and the lamb which denote the future toil of their fallen state. The Third Person of the Trinity is usually seen in the form of a dove, while the Trinity itself may be indicated by the symbol of a triangle (see p. 184) or by the three

Fig. 54.—Carved ivory panel from a book-cover, with the Nativity and Adoration: sixth century. (*Catalogue of Ivory Carvings*, No. 14.)

angels who appeared to Abraham (Gen. xviii): the latter is the general type in East-Christian art of all periods.

Of *Saints*, the most frequently represented in early times were the Apostles Peter and Paul, usually found in conjunction. In their case we find characterization even before the fourth century, St. Peter almost always having thick hair and a short beard, St. Paul a long beard and bald head. It may be added as a point of interest that the earliest attribute of St. Peter is a scroll or a staff with a cross at the end, the key or keys not appearing until the fifth century; while that of St. Paul is also a scroll, the sword not being assigned him until the tenth. The rest of the Apostles were not characterized by special traits until the sixth century. Among the Saints most frequently represented in the fourth and fifth centuries are St. Agnes and St. Lawrence, who are often found upon the gilded glasses.

The Crucifixion on a large scale, easily seen, is rather later than upon gems; we have noted the symbolic style persisting in the fourth century upon sarcophagi in the Lateran (p. 84). No direct representation of the scene on a larger scale than that of gems appears to have survived from the fourth century; but a passage in the contemporary Christian poet, Prudentius, describes the Crucifixion between the two thieves, apparently as a subject adapted for the decoration of a church. Perhaps the earliest existing example is the carved ivory panel from a casket in the Museum Collection (plate II), of which a cast is seen in Wall-Case 3 (original among the ivory carvings in the King Edward VII Gallery, Bay XX, Table-Case); the work dates from the very beginning of the fifth century, if not from the last years of the fourth. On the gems, the figure of Christ was nude or semi-nude; here there is a narrow loin-cloth, as in the Crucifixion between the two Thieves on the carved wooden doors of St. Sabina at Rome, which are not very much later than the ivory. The almost nude type appears to have continued in succeeding centuries, though only in rare examples, for in the sixth century there seems to have been a feeling against realistic treatment. The figure of Our Lord is now often draped, generally in a sleeveless tunic reaching to the ankles, known as a *colobium*. This garment is seen on a pendant for the neck of the sixth century at Monza, in the often-quoted miniature in the Syriac gospels of Rabula, and in a later mural painting of St. Maria Antiqua at Rome (early eighth century). From the ninth century onwards, the *colobium* is generally replaced by a broad loin-cloth, though it survives by exception

Fig. 55. — Engraved gem: the Crucifixion. (No. 43.)

at a later date. The mosaics of the older churches in Rome, Ravenna, and Constantinople do not include the Crucifixion, though the above-mentioned verses of Prudentius and the description by Choricius (A. D. 527–65) of the church of St. Sergius at Gaza (p. 29) seem to show that the subject was permitted to the mosaicist or the painter. During part of the seventh century there appear still to have been objections to realism, especially in the West; but with the beginning of the eighth century, as a result of the Council *In Trullo*, held at Constantinople in A. D. 692, the subject was formally accepted by the Church.

Even upon the earliest gems, subsidiary figures are seen beside the cross. These primitive gems have a row on either side; the British Museum ivory shows the Virgin and St. John on one side, the centurion Longinus on the other. In the Gospels of Rabula these figures are again seen, with the addition of the sponge-bearer Stephaton, three holy women, the soldiers casting lots for the garment at the foot of the cross, the personified Sun and Moon above the arms. In St. Maria Antiqua there are again several figures, the Virgin and St. John, Longinus and Stephaton; the composition, though less elaborate, still represents a Syrian type destined to yet further amplification in the picturesque developments of Carolingian art which derives so much from Syrian inspiration. After the period of iconoclasm the Byzantine composition assumed its final form: the Sun and Moon are seen above the Cross; to right and left stand the Virgin and St. John; at the foot is always the skull of Adam, in allusion to the tradition that the cross was erected on the spot where the first man was buried.

In the earliest Crucifixions the figure of Christ stands on the ground, or upon a foot-rest fixed to the lower limb of the cross; this latter feature, known as the *suppedaneum*, is indicated in the British Museum ivory, and is universal in Byzantine art after the ninth century. But in the Syrian type of Crucifixion mentioned above, the feet are nailed directly to the cross (gospels of Rabula, St. Maria Antiqua). In all this early work they are side by side, and fixed by two nails. The crossed feet, fixed by a single nail, belong only to the West, and are first found at the beginning of the thirteenth century.

At the end of these brief iconographical notes it will be convenient to say a word on the *costume* of sacred persons in Christian art. Our Lord and the Apostles and Saints are almost always clothed in an ungirded, long-sleeved tunic reaching to the feet, and in a long mantle called a *pallium*, one end of which was thrown forward over the left shoulder so as to reach to the ankle, while the rest was drawn round the back, under the right shoulder and across the body, the second end being draped over the left fore-arm (plate II). The right arm was thus left free, but the left was encumbered, and the dress was therefore unsuited for active exertion. This mantle was a Greek garment, once characteristic of philosophers, and was contrasted with the national Roman toga, which was draped in a different way. In process of time it was superseded by other outer garments of a more practical kind such as the *paenula* or *planeta*, a poncho with a hole in the middle for the head, or the *lacerna*, a kind of cloak fastened by a brooch over the breast; but it survived as a ceremonial or official garb in the form of a narrow folded band, which, according to a very plausible theory, in time became the Archbishop's pallium of the Roman Catholic Church. In the upper part of plate II, Our Lord is seen wearing the tunic and pallium as above described, with the sandals which usually accompany this costume. The tunic and pallium likewise form the costume of Angels, who appear as beautiful youths, and are at first usually represented as wingless, though with the lapse of time the addition of wings became the rule: the small nude winged figures which are occasionally found on objects used by Christians are simply the genii of Roman art, and used with a decorative purpose; the child-angel is the invention of comparatively modern art. Another outer garment is a long mantle fastened with a brooch upon the right shoulder so as to leave both arms free though the left was concealed. This mantle, the usual garb of military and official persons, is called the *chlamys*, and may be seen on plates II, VII, and IX; it was never adopted by the Church.

Another garment to which attention may be drawn is the *dalmatica*, a long outer tunic of wool or linen with vertical stripes (*clavi*), usually purple, down the front, and other ornamental patches (*segmenta, calliculae*), near the lower border and on the shoulders; it was sometimes worn out of doors without a mantle, and the popularity of this custom probably encouraged the growth of elaborate embroidered ornamentation. Female costume consisted of a long tunic reaching to the ankles and a mantle similar to the pallium, called a *palla*, the end of which, when a veil was not used, was often drawn over the head like a hood, instead of passing under the right arm.

Persons of inferior rank wore shorter girded tunics which, in the case of orientals, were often drawn up at the waist so as to form a deep hanging fold concealing the girdle. Orientals also wore, in addition to a short chlamys, tightly fitting breeches reaching to the ankles, and the so-called Phrygian cap. Examples of this are seen in the figures of Daniel and of the soldier decapitating St. Menas, both on plate IV. In the early representations of the Adoration, the Magi wear this costume; they do not appear as Kings until mediaeval times. Jews, in Early Christian art, are sometimes depicted in round caps with flat tops (plate II).

The above secular garments have more than a passing interest, through the fact that out of them developed ecclesiastical vestments, some of which have been in continuous use from Early Christian times (p. 115).

III. CHURCHES AND THEIR CONTENTS.

(For Early Christian churches in Britain *see* p. 61.)

a. The buildings. The subject of architecture in the earlier Christian centuries and its relation to that of the Middle Ages in the West is too wide and too controversial to be more than touched upon in the present place. In Italy and the Hellenistic area comprising the coast-lands of the Eastern Mediterranean, the first Christian churches took the form of the *basilica*, a Greek word literally meaning 'royal hall'. The earlier assemblies of Christians had taken place in large rooms in the houses of aristocratic or wealthy converts; the chambers or small chapels in the catacombs, though certainly used for memorial services, can hardly have accommodated general congregations. In contemporary Rome the word basilica had been applied to any large covered hall, but more especially to the *basilica iudiciaria* or law-court, which was a development of the old open forum or market-place. But although the forensic basilica was the most conspicuous member of the class, it is now generally held that it was not the immediate prototype of the Christian building, for it did not regularly combine all the characteristics by which the earliest Christian churches are marked. Archaeologists still differ as to the origin of the Christian basilica, and the number of theories which have been put forward is too great for discussion in this place. It must suffice to say that some regard the basilica as derived from

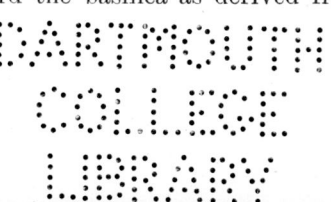

Hellenistic sources; others see in it a development of the central court (*atrium*) of the ordinary Roman dwelling-house; while others, again, seek its origin in the large halls attached to the houses of great nobles and officials, in the small catacomb chapels, or in an extension of the little apsed oratories, *cellae cœmeteriales*, erected for commemorative services in the area of the cemeteries: it is suggested that these *cellae*, which on one side had nothing but columns, were also used for regular services in early times, the clergy standing beneath them, and the people before them in the open air; and that after the peace of the Church a long nave with aisles, the idea of which

FIG. 56.—Exterior of old St. Peter's, Rome.

was borrowed from secular buildings, was added for the convenience of the congregation.

The Roman basilica was a rectangular building with a timbered roof, consisting of a high nave divided on each side by a row of columns from two low lateral aisles. Each of these was itself sometimes subdivided by an additional row of columns; the nave walls were pierced by rows of clerestory windows. The roof was covered with lead, or with bronze or terracotta tiles. But as the church was usually surrounded by other buildings, the only part of the exterior which needed adornment was the façade; even this was partially concealed by the narthex, forming one side of a court (*atrium*) surrounded by porticoes, and having in the middle a fountain (*cantharus, phiale*) for washing the hands.

In the early centuries of Christianity the practice of immersion at baptism was universal, and a large basin or *piscina* was required. As this could not be conveniently placed in the church, detached circular or octagonal buildings called baptisteries were erected, the *piscina* being sunk in the floor. This practice was general until after the sixth century; when it went out of use, the font was placed first in the narthex and ultimately inside the church.

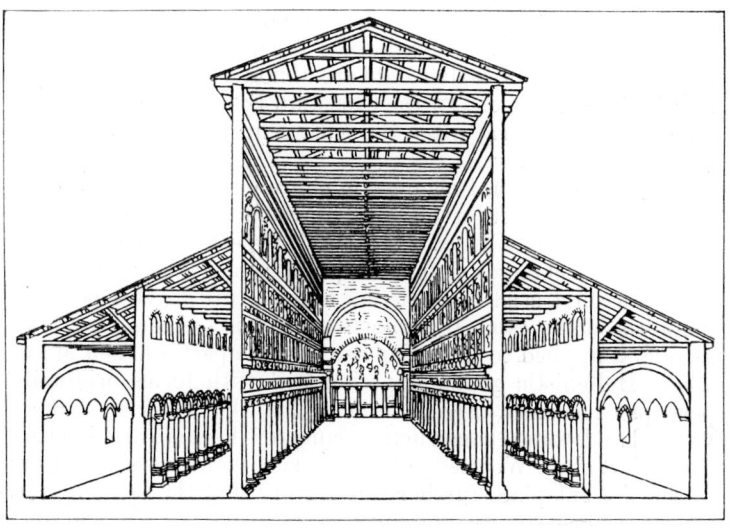

Fig. 57.—Interior of old St Peter's, Rome.

Round the sides of early churches there were often a number of small chapels (*cubicula*), sometimes used as places of burial. Figs. 56 and 57 showing the old St. Peter's at Rome, replaced by the modern cathedral in the early sixteenth century, illustrate many of the characteristics of the basilica which have been enumerated above.

The basilica naturally developed different features in so wide an area as that comprising the countries round the Eastern Mediterranean, Italy, and the West in general. These are too detailed to be enumerated here; it should be noticed, however, that where, east of the Mediterranean, the Hellenistic type penetrated into the interior, as in Syria, parts of Asia

Minor, and Northern Mesopotamia, modifications were more pronounced, and bore a definitely oriental character. Thus the western façade might have two towers between which the narthex shrank to a kind of loggia, while the atrium was generally abolished. In the volcanic district of the Hauran, south of Damascus, where timber was difficult to obtain but basaltic stone abundant, the whole building was of stone, long slabs of stone replacing timber in the construction of the roof.

The basilica with timber roof had an area of distribution ranging from the Greek area in North Syria and Asia Minor to Great Britain. In Rome, Italy, and the West it remained continuously in favour until the close of the first millennium, when churches with vaulted roofs became general; the few vaulted churches of earlier date are abnormal, and perhaps due to oriental influence. In the Christian East the basilican plan ceased to be general after the fifth century, but survived in exceptional cases.

The most important changes in church architecture resulted from the introduction of vaulted roofs and the placing of domes over square bays. It is still a matter of controversy where these changes first took place, some holding that the vault was first used in Christian architecture in Mesopotamia while the dome came from northern Persia; others that both were first applied to Christian use in those parts of Asia Minor where Hellenistic genius experimented with forms originally perhaps of eastern origin; others that the whole system of vaulted and domed construction came to Christian architecture through Rome. We need not discuss such controversial matters in the present place further than to say that the barrel vault, the first form to be employed, was certainly known long before the Christian Era both in Mesopotamia and in Egypt, and that the dome over a square plan was also used several centuries before Christ in the case of tombs or mausolea. At present the earliest dated church for congregational use which had the vaulted roof is one of the ruined churches at Binbirkilisse in Isauria in the south-east of Asia Minor, belonging to the fifth century; but other ruins without precise date may well go back into the fourth. The dome over a square bay was incorporated with the vaulted basilica at very much the same time, the earliest example for which there is any precise evidence of date being the ruined church of St. Thekla at Meriamlik near the Cilician Seleucia, ascribed to the fourth century; another church at Khoja Kalessi in Isauria is very probably of much the same age.

PLATE VII.—TOP OF THE SILVER BRIDAL CASKET OF PROJECTA: PORTRAITS OF THE BRIDE AND BRIDEGROOM.

In addition to long basilican churches, various forms of centralized buildings were erected from the fourth century onwards, chiefly, as above noted, for use as baptisteries or small chapels. These buildings, which in Italy and the Hellenistic area were round or octagonal in plan, were either timber-roofed, like St. Stefano Rotondo at Rome, or domed, like St. Costanza in the same city. Buildings of this type were less well adapted for congregational use than long churches; for even in the case of advanced types like St. Vitale at Ravenna, the piers tend to obstruct the view. The domed examples are therefore of less importance in the history of development than aisled churches with domes, to the improvement of which for liturgical and congregational use the invention of architects was directed.

Cruciform churches were probably intended to affirm the significance of the cross as a symbol of the faith. The tendency to suggest the cross in church plans came into prominence in the fifth century, and is even marked in the form of basilica in which the ends of transepts project beyond the sides of the nave. But the regular cruciform churches were of two principal types: (1) that in which the whole building resembles a free-standing cross, like the (now destroyed) Church of the Apostles at Constantinople, built in the reign of Justinian, or St. Mark's at Venice, which reproduces its plan: this type is derived by some from a catacomb form; (2) that often described as the Greek-Cross church (*église à croix grecque, Kreuzkuppelkirche*). The former type is of less importance because it never became very general, and did not win lasting popularity in the Christian East. It is necessary to say a few words on the latter, because from the close of the ninth century until the fall of the Empire it was the characteristic Byzantine type, and having spread beyond the frontiers, into other countries of the Orthodox Eastern Church, continued to influence their architecture down to modern times. The name is at first sight inappropriate, since at the ground level the church has the appearance of a square building (*see* below).

The origin of the Greek-Cross type is not certainly known. Some authorities derive it from the domed basilica, holding that the cross-form was produced by the addition of barrel-vaulted transepts to resist the thrust of the dome on the north and south sides. Others derive it from pagan buildings in which two vaulted halls intersect each other at right angles, for the square bay at the crossing, actually covered by other kinds of roofing, might easily, they think, have suggested to men acquainted with domical buildings the substitution of a dome. The most recent suggestion is that of Strzygowski, that the Greek-Cross church is of Armenian origin. Armenian church architecture seems from the first to have employed the dome over the square bay as its unit, and a development of this unit, so as to make the dome rest not on the four outer walls, but on

Fig. 58.—Exterior of the Church of the Apostles, Salonika (after Texier and Pullan).

four inner supports, might readily give rise to a plan resembling that of the Greek-Cross within its enclosing walls. The earliest Armenian example of which the date is known is the ruined church at Bagaran erected in A.D. 624; and it is pointed out that the first building of the type recorded at Constantinople was the *Nea* or New Church built in the grounds of the Great Palace for the Emperor Basil I (A.D. 867–86), himself an Armenian. Whatever the origin of the type, its popularity dates from the time of Basil, and it ended by assuming a predominant and almost exclusive position in East-Christian church building. As already noticed, on the ground level it presents the appearance of a square building, because the angles of the cross are filled by four subsidiary chambers, thrown open on their inner sides, thus providing two aisles, a *prothesis* and a *diakonikon*, rooms adjoining the *bema* (p. 100) to North and South, the first used for preparing the bread and wine, the second as a vestry. But since these chambers are lower than the nave and transepts, the cruciform shape is visible on the outside above the level of their roofs; thus, although the Greek-Cross type in its ground plan resembles a cross inscribed in a square, in its upper part its form accords with its name. The central dome did not stand alone. Others were added, usually over the angle-chambers, so that the typical Byzantine church has commonly five, of which that in the centre, in examples of the eleventh century and later, rises like a tower (fig. 58).

In the West the dome was never popular except for baptisteries and memorial churches until the Renaissance, when its introduction by Italian architects may have been due to fresh oriental influences. The earlier domed mediaeval churches which were erected were due to the imitation of oriental models. St. Germigny-les-Prés, near Orleans, was built in the ninth century, and the cathedral of St. Mark's at Venice in the eleventh. It remains to notice the domed churches in Périgueux, where the cathedral of St. Front reproduces the plan of St. Mark's and therefore, at second remove, that of the Church of the Apostles at Constantinople.

Belfries were earlier in the West than in the East, the oldest known being apparently the round tower of St. Apollinare Nuovo at Ravenna, built in the second half of the ninth century: where found in connexion with Byzantine churches, the belfry may be regarded as a proof of western influence. Church bells, which probably originated in monasteries, were commonly used in the West as early as the sixth century; a well-known passage in Bede's *Ecclesiastical History* relates how one of St. Hilda's nuns knew of the saint's death while at some distance from Whitby by hearing the sound of the passing bell; and we learn from Gregory of Tours that in sixth-century Gaul not only monasteries but parish churches possessed bells. But in the churches of the East the bell was not adopted so early; its place was taken by the *simantron* (σημάντρον), or *simandra*, a thick slab either of wood or stone,

H

suspended by a cord and struck by a piece of wood or iron. The first church bells used in Constantinople were sent as a gift by Ursus, Doge of Venice, to the Emperor Michael about A.D. 865. The general employment of the bell did not, however, come in until after the Latin occupation of Constantinople in the thirteenth century; even then the *simantron* was not discarded, and it has survived until modern times in Greek monasteries and in Abyssinian and Coptic churches. It may be added that church bells seem to have been preceded by hand-bells (*tintinnabula*), used at an early date in monasteries, and by the first missionaries as a means of summoning to service: the ancient iron bells associated with the names of the Irish Saints are of this nature.

Fig. 59.—Church of Amba Derho, Abyssinia (after J. T. Bent, *The Sacred City of the Ethiopians*).

In conclusion a brief mention may be made of the Coptic churches of Egypt and those of Abyssinia. The exterior of the Coptic church, usually obscured by other buildings, has commonly a number of domes or cupolas, but there appears to be no definite cruciform plan; the dark interior with its aisle and two naves suggests a basilica rather than a cross-church. It has three apses which are not seen from outside. The Abyssinian church seems to be of independent development. It is a circular building with conical thatched roof, the exterior resembling that of the native hut from which it is probably derived. Its sanctuary is in the middle, while round it are two concentric zones separated by walls, that nearest the sanctuary for priests, the other for the congregation.

Reviewing the above paragraphs in connexion with those relating to English churches (p. 61), we find that the timber-roofed basilica ranged from Syria to Britain, where the small example of which the foundations were discovered at Silchester was built in the Roman city on that site (Calleva) in the fourth century. The timber-roofed basilica remained the common form of church in Italy and France until about the year A.D. 1000, when vaulted roofing came in and the Romanesque style began. The origin of roof vaulting in western Romanesque churches is contested, some ascribing it to the revival of Roman traditions by the architects of Lombardy towards A.D. 1000, others believing that the inspiration came directly from the Christian East several centuries earlier. In England, after an interval caused by the Saxon invasions, the basilican plan was re-introduced by St. Augustine's Roman Mission, and remains of seventh-century examples survive (p. 63). But in these islands a simpler single-halled type of Celtic origin, pressing down from the north, met and overcame the basilica, and to this single-halled type the Saxon churches in England, as a class, belong (p. 64): when the three-aisled basilican plan was re-introduced a second time, it came in a modified form as the vaulted Norman church. In most countries circular or octagonal Christian buildings were built as early as basilicas, and domed examples of the fourth century survive.

In the Christian East, the introduction of vaulted single-halled or basilican churches is traced by different authorities to Mesopotamia, the Hellenistic area in western Asia, and to Rome: wherever they originated, such churches were probably built in the fifth century, or even earlier. Domed long churches must have begun about the same period, and were prevalent in the sixth century, when a domed cruciform type was represented by the large church of the Apostles at Constantinople, now destroyed. The cruciform church known as the Greek-Cross type, characteristic of Byzantine architecture, became common after the ninth century (p. 95).

The domed long church was not a western form until the high Renaissance in Italy in the late sixteenth century. It did not belong either to the Romanesque or to the Gothic style, which did not roof central towers with domes; the early domed cruciform churches which stand on western soil are abnormal, and due to special eastern influences. In England, St. Paul's Cathedral, built by Wren at the close of the seventeenth century, is the earliest domed long church.

b. Interior arrangement and decoration. The interior arrangement of a basilica was somewhat as follows. The altar stood across the chord of the apse. In the early churches, only the space within the apse, called *bema* or *presbyterium*, was available for the clergy, who sat on stone benches (*subsellia*), following the curve of the apse, the bishop's chair (*cathedra*) being in the middle at the back, directly facing the altar, which stood free. Low marble screens (*cancelli*) railed off the apse from the nave. When there was a transept, as was often the case in large churches, it was separated from the nave by a massive arch, and the *cancelli* were brought forward to the line dividing the transept from aisles and nave. Where there was no transept, the increased demand for room for the clergy in some cases necessitated the extension of the *bema* beyond the apsidal arch, and often also the railing-in of the ends of the aisles. At the end of the nave nearest the altar was a central space reserved for the choir, which was itself railed in by *cancelli*; and within the nave on one side of this screen, sometimes on both, was an *ambon* or *ambo*, a high stone pulpit used for reading the lections, as well as for sermons when these were no longer delivered from the apse. The congregation was accommodated in the aisles, the men and women on different sides, the latter overflowing into the back of the nave if occasion required; but where the aisles had an upper gallery, this was usually reserved for women. Catechumens were placed at the back of the nave, and penitents in the porch or *narthex* (see plan, fig. 60). Greek and Roman basilicas were chiefly lighted by the clerestory windows, which were usually filled with pierced stone slabs: windows were also frequently placed in the apse and over the door at the opposite end of the building. The walls of the aisles were blind, but at Ravenna and in eastern churches of the basilican type, there were windows in the aisles also. In important churches the larger surfaces of the walls were covered with brilliant mosaics; the columns and *cancelli* were of marble, with which stone the walls of the aisles were also faced; and the floor was usually covered with marble slabs. The gable roof was hidden by a carved and gilded wooden ceiling placed just above the clerestory, which, owing to the nature of its windows, admitted a soft diffused light admirably calculated to heighten the effect of the mosaics and gilding. It was upon the interior of the basilica that all the decoration was lavished; the exterior was of plain brickwork.

In Byzantine churches of the more sumptuous kind, the chief splendour, as in the early basilicas, was reserved for the interior. In the regions where churches were built of brick, the contrast between the comparatively unadorned exterior and the inside walls and roofs, rich with ornament and colour, was even more marked than where stone was the material. But after the tenth century the contrast between plain exterior and gorgeous interior was less accentuated: more and more attention was given to exteriors, which were enriched by the

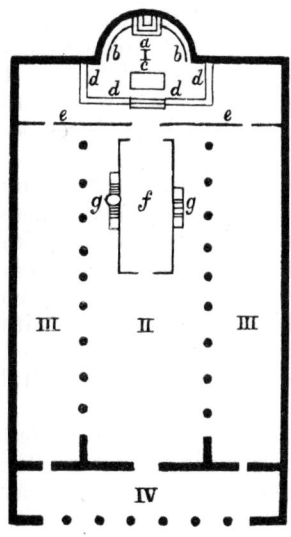

Fig. 60.—Plan of a basilica. I. *Presbyterium.* II. *Nave.* III. *Aisles.* IV. *Narthex.* *a.* Bishop's chair. *bb.* Seats for clergy. *c.* Altar. *dd, ee.* Cancelli. *f.* Choir. *gg.* Ambons.

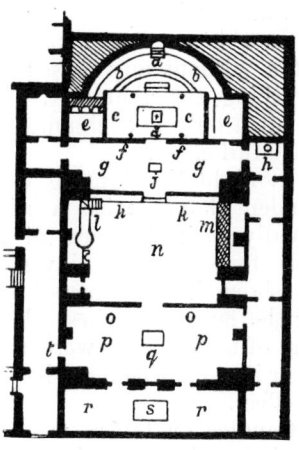

Fig. 61.— Plan of the Coptic church of Abu-'s-Sifain, Cairo (after Butler, *Ancient Coptic Churches of Egypt*). *a.* Patriarchal Throne. *bb.* Marble bench for priests. *cc. Haikal* or sanctuary. *d.* Altar. *ee.* Lateral sanctuaries. *ff. Haikal* screen. *gg.* Choir. *h.* Font. *j.* Lectern. *kk.* Screen. *l.* Pulpit. *m.* Locker for relics. *n.* Men's division. *oo.* Screen. *pp.* Women's division. *q.* Tank in which the priest annually washes the feet of the poor. *rr.* Narthex. *s.* Epiphany tank, formerly used for baptism at Epiphany. *t.* Door.

developed use of alternating bands of brick and stone, geometrical arrangements of brick, recessed window-arches, and other features. Where ample funds were available the method of decoration in brick churches was much the same at all periods. The lower walls were covered with a lining of coloured marbles, and the upper with glass mosaic, which, if the church was vaulted, also extended over the vaults. The columns were of coloured marble, with white marble sculptured capitals; the closure-slabs limiting the chancel and the galleries, where such existed, were also of white marble, usually carved with conventional designs in low relief. The churches of poorer communities were covered in the interior with stucco, on which were painted designs corresponding to those executed in mosaic in richer buildings. In the East, windows were not, as in the comparatively gloomy North and West, large and filled with stained glass, but small, and formed of slabs of marble or stucco, pierced at intervals with round holes, often without any glass; in hot climates, where light was if anything too abundant, the function of a window was to admit it only in such amount as to allow mosaics and frescoes their full effect.

At night the lighting of interiors was chiefly effected by pendent lamps with a number of separate lights. These usually took the form of flat openwork bronze disks with holes for small glass oil vessels: examples of these *polycandela* are shown in Wall-Cases 1 and 2. Though the light given even by the largest of these objects would be dim compared with that of to-day, they were often employed in such numbers that their illumination must have been both adequate and beautiful in effect.

Candles or tapers were doubtless used from the earliest Christian times: we have mention of them in the catacombs; in early churches they must have stood upon altars, and may have been fixed to the ciboria above them. Candelabra with three feet are represented in early frescoes, and the candles seem to have been indifferently fixed either in sockets or upon upright spikes or prickets. Bronze oil-lamps were also used upon candelabra, a cavity in the base receiving the pricket. (Examples of the sixth century in Wall-Cases 1 and 2.)

The interior division and arrangement of Christian churches had at all periods many common features, though in course of time variations were naturally developed In Byzantine churches, and in those of the Orthodox Greek Church generally, the *bema* or sanctuary, and the *prothesis* and *diakonikon* (p. 97) are separated from the body of the church not by low *cancelli* but by a high screen with three entrances, the double central doors leading into the sanctuary itself, the other two doors into the lateral chambers. This screen, known as the *iconostasis*, from the fact that *ikons* or sacred pictures were fixed to its panels, might be made of any material, and in important churches was sometimes of carved marble, or even of precious metals; in the Greek Church it has in recent

CHURCHES AND THEIR CONTENTS 103

centuries been of richly carved and gilded wood. The doors of the iconostasis played their part in the processions of the clergy, and there is a theory that its architectural form and the arrangement of its doors were suggested by the proscenium of the ancient theatre, itself reproducing a palace façade.

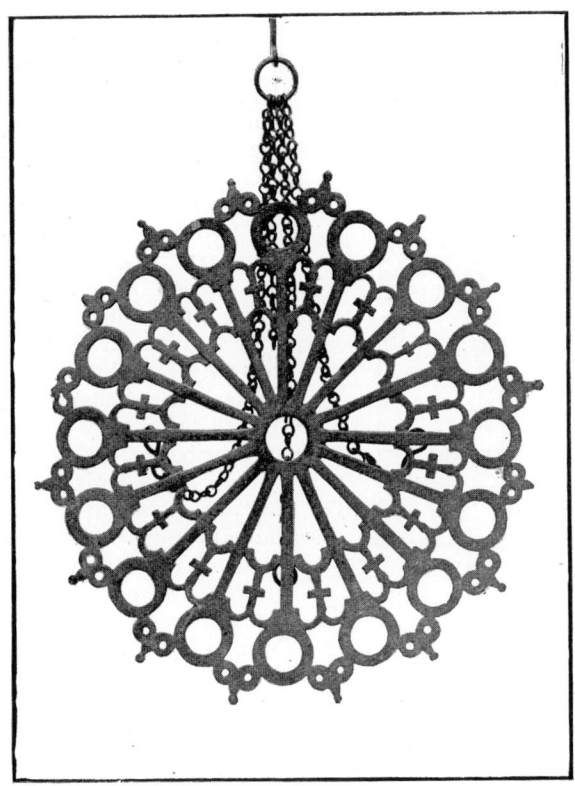

Fig. 62.—Bronze hanging disk for lamps (*polycandelon*) : sixth century. (No. 529.)

The altar was covered, from as early as the fourth century, by a high canopy or *ciborium* (cf. fig. 63), which again was often of costly material, marble or precious metal, with rich columns between which curtains were hung. In branches of the Orthodox Greek Church this canopy ceased to be an independent structure, and is now a miniature copy, the columns of which do not rest on the ground, but on the altar itself. The *ambon* or pulpit was outside the screen in the eastern part of the nave as in the early basilicas. The galleries, which sometimes extended across the narthex, were reserved for women, and were therefore known as *gynaecea*. It is a peculiarity of Coptic interiors (fig. 61) that the nave is divided into three parts by two screens additional to that corresponding to the iconostasis, which encloses the sanctuary or *haikal*. The first of these, commonly latticed, but sometimes with pictures along the top, separates the choir which is immediately outside the sanctuary screen, from the rest of the nave. The second divides the body of the nave into two parts, that nearer the sanctuary reserved for men, that beyond it for women.

The kind of subjects or ornament applied to church walls naturally varied with the views and fashions of changing times. When Christianity issued from the period of suppression to become a recognized religion, the old symbolic system of the catacombs was superseded (p. 27). The first need of the Church was now to celebrate its victory and give visible form to its history and dogma. For this purpose it replaced the allusive and indirect symbolism of the earlier periods by a historic and dogmatic art. The events of sacred story could now be directly set before the eyes of the faithful, and the Fathers were quick to perceive the assistance which art could render, not only by quickening the interest of those who could read, but by giving instruction to those who could not. At first it was evidently usual in some districts to cover the walls of churches with paintings, apparently quite secular, but possibly with symbolic associations of oriental origin (p. 24). But with the lapse of time and the growing organization of the Church, this usage, perhaps influenced from Persian sources, was generally abandoned, and in the course of the fifth cen-

FIG. 63.—Altar with ciborium: North Italian, ninth century (after Rohault de Fleury).

tury we find a historical and dogmatic art fairly established, largely under monastic auspices and the influence of Syrian theology (p. 28). The expanses of wall above the nave columns were painted with scenes from the Old and New Testament. The apse and its arch received subjects derived from the Apocalypse, representing Our Lord in Glory, surrounded by saints and martyrs, the Lamb, and other figures suggesting the glories of the life to come; or, as at St. Maria Maggiore in Rome, subjects of dogmatic significance. By the sixth century, when the imperial power at Byzantium had reached its height, and State and Church were closely allied, we mark the intrusion of scenes representing imperial persons into the very *bema*, as when, at St. Vitale at Ravenna, Justinian and Theodora with their courtiers appear in the immediate neighbourhood of Old Testament scenes typifying the Eucharistic Sacrifice. After the Persian and Arab wars, iconoclasm interrupted the progress of church decoration. There was a reversion in some cases to the secular scenes above described; these were used in the nave, while in the apse a simple cross seems to have replaced the figures of Our Lord or of the Virgin. After the restoration of sacred pictures, the re-establishment of a strong dynasty made it possible to reorganize the development of church painting. This was done under the monastic influence which throughout the long struggle had championed the cause of pictures; a liturgical direction was now given to the scheme of decoration, and the subjects upon church walls were brought into an intimate relation to the rite celebrated within them. The whole arrangement was more strictly ordered; it was no longer possible for imperial persons or founders to be represented on the sanctuary walls; they were relegated to more humble places in the body of the building or even in the narthex. In quite early times different parts of the church had possessed their own meaning. But now the symbolism became more precise, and the decoration which each received more exactly accorded with its meaning. The dome and the *bema* represented the celestial world, the rest of the church the terrestrial. The subjects, whether painted or in mosaic, were brought into harmony with these ideas. In the crown of the dome was the figure of Christ *Pantokrator*, or Lord of All; below Him, forming a circle, were archangels, apostles, or prophets. In the apse of the *bema* was the Virgin, commonly with hands raised in the ancient attitude of prayer and interceding for the world, or seated with the Child on her knees; on the walls and in the secondary apses were the antitypes of Christ, subjects representative of the Eucharist, and Old Testament scenes prefiguring it; on the vault might be the empty throne prepared for the second coming, together with the Instruments of the Passion. In the body of the building, the upper walls were adorned with Gospel scenes illustrating the events in the life of Our Lord and the Virgin commemorated in the Twelve Feasts of the Church (usually the Annunciation, Nativity, Presentation in the Temple, Baptism, Raising of Lazarus, Transfiguration, Entry into Jerusalem, Crucifixion, Descent into Hell, Pentecost, and Death of the Virgin). Below these, in long rows, were the saints and martyrs. The ideas underlying the whole scheme were the pre-eminence of the supersensible world and the central importance of the rite. Historical sequence was abandoned for an order exactly consistent with liturgical requirement.

c. Objects of ecclesiastical use. The above short account of architectural types may be conveniently followed by a few facts as to the objects used in the services of the church. Chief among these were the *chalice* and the *paten*. The form and size of the chalice varied in the course of centuries, as did the material of which it was made. The early chalices naturally adopted already familiar forms. They were usually but not always of the *cantharus* type with two handles, and were often of glass, sometimes coloured. In the fresco in the Roman catacombs known as the *Fractio Panis*, the chalice represented has two handles, but not the foot which soon became general, and is seen in the examples of blue glass from Amiens, probably, if not certainly, used as chalices (Wall-Cases 5 and 6, fig. 64). Other forms were contemporary with the handled type. An epitaph from the Roman Catacombs, copied by Boldetti, was accompanied by a chalice without handles, but having a knop and comparatively high foot. In early times there was a distinction in size between the chalices used by the celebrants and those in which the wine was distributed to the faithful; these latter were much larger, and described as greater, or 'ministerial'. Chalices of silver and gold seem to have been in use as early as about A. D. 300; those of glass may in general have characterized the times of persecution, though they were still made in later times: one of the legends relating to St. Patrick makes mention of glass chalices. After the Peace of the Church, we read of chalices of precious metal, enriched by gems, given by Constantine to various churches, and St. Jerome speaks of others cut from hard stone, probably onyx or agate; but in the West the sack of

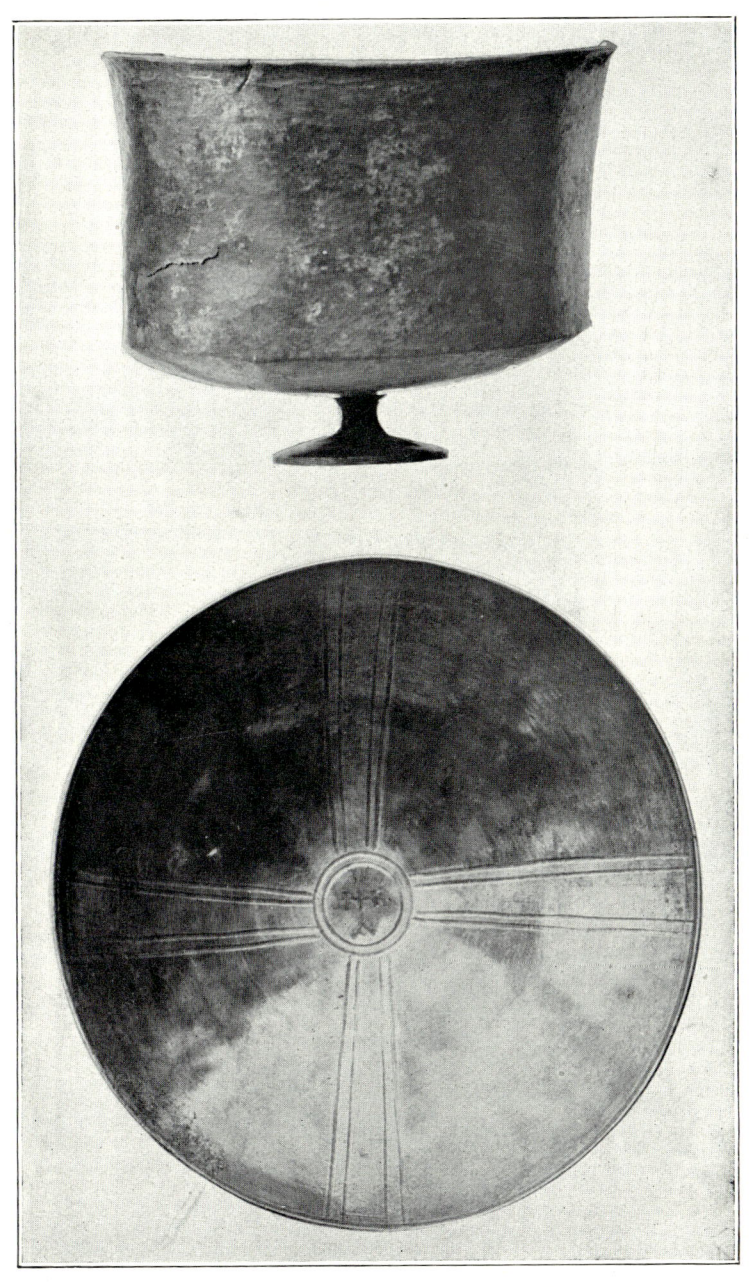

PLATE VIII. BYZANTINE SILVER TREASURE FROM LAMPSACUS. SIXTH CENTURY.
(*See* p. 175.)

Rome by the Goths and the impoverishment of the fifth century led for a time to the general use of plain silver. The costlier examples at this time were made in the Christian East.

The mosaics and sarcophagi of the fifth and sixth centuries show the two-handled form of chalice still in favour. It is seen, for example, on the mosaics of St. Vitale and St. Apollinare in Classe at Ravenna, where in one case a gold chalice covered with precious stones is depicted. The gold chalice in the treasure of Gourdon, in France, which has two handles, and round the upper part a band of foliated ornament inlaid with turquoise and red stones or pastes, belongs to the first part of the sixth century, and is either of early Teutonic workmanship reproducing oriental methods, or, as some think, itself of East-Christian origin. The two-handled type seems

Fig. 64.—Glass vessel from Amiens, perhaps a chalice, 5th–6th century. (No. 658.)

to have been obligatory in the time of Gregory the Great (A.D. 590–604), and chalices now lost, but once in the treasury of the cathedral of Monza, had this form. Here again the reproductions which have come down to us suggest gold and gems, which the barbaric courts of the Goths, Lombards, and Franks were now able to afford. The type survived to a later date both in the West and in the East; the well-known chalice of Ardagh in Ireland is of the eighth or ninth century; that of St. Gauzelin at Nancy of the tenth; two-handled examples are also found among the Byzantine chalices at Venice (p. 110). The other early type with knop and foot, but without handles, also persisted. An example belonging to the church of Zamon near Trent appears to date from the sixth century; the gold chalice associated with the name of St. Eloi (Eligius), formerly at Chelles, but destroyed at the time of the French Revolution, was of this form, as were a bronze example with the name of St. Chrodegand of Séez (*d.* A. D. 775), now in Russia, and another eighth-century example at Werden in Westphalia. The silver chalice of Tassilo Duke of Bavaria, preserved at Kremsmünster in Upper Austria, belongs to the second half of the eighth century; it bears ornament of the character introduced into Franconia by Celtic missionaries from Ireland (p. 60), has no handles, an almost spherical knop, and conical foot. The ninth-century chalice from Trewhiddle (fig. 39 and p. 68) conforms to this

FIG. 65.—Inscribed silver chalice, probably from Syria: sixth century.

general type. In these early chalices with bowl, knop, and round foot, we have the prototypes from which the usual Romanesque and mediaeval types developed.

Among surviving chalices from the Christian East, the two-handled form is not represented among antiquities of the earlier Christian centuries, though, as we have seen in the case of the Ravenna mosaics, it must certainly have been in use. The oldest existing eastern chalices have a bowl without handles, a knop, and foot. The present collection contains a large example of the sixth century with a votive inscription round the rim (fig. 65); it resembles an example at present

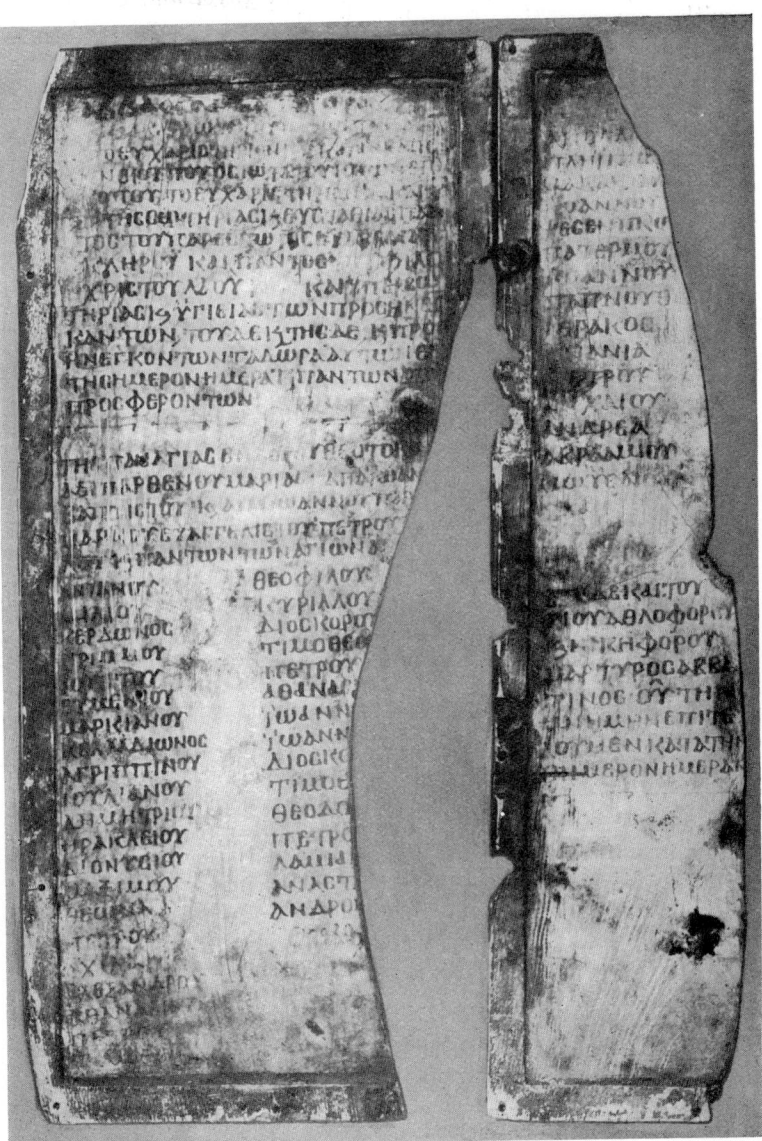

Fig. 66.—Ivory liturgical diptych from Egypt: seventh century; see p. 114.

in Paris, found in Northern Syria in 1910, and engraved with a consecration formula. Another silver cup, not so certainly a chalice, forms part of the treasure of Lampsacus (plate VIII).

The best examples of Byzantine chalices are those in the treasury of St. Mark's at Venice, whither they were brought after the capture of Constantinople in A.D. 1204; here the type with large hemispherical bowl, and the two-handled variety, both occur. But these chalices, which have bowls of alabaster, onyx or agate, gilt or gold mounts, and rich ornament of gems, pearls, and enamelled plaques, do not represent the possessions of ordinary churches but of wealthy or famous foundations in the capital, and are of an exceptionally sumptuous kind. Several have the usual words of administration in Greek round the rim.

The earliest patens were perhaps of glass, like the chalices; few of the 'gilded glasses' (p. 140) are supposed to have been patens, including, in the view of some authorities, the remarkable glass disk found at Cologne (Table-Case B and fig. 91). When chalices began to be of metal, patens naturally followed suit, and it may be assumed that they were generally circular, as seen in the mosaics at Ravenna, though this does not necessarily follow (see below). Nor need they have been always flat; it is conjectured that the two rather small shallow bowls in the Lampsacus treasure (plate VIII) may have been patens.

Early patens were often decorated with a variety of subjects in relief. An example of the sixth century found in North Syria has upon it Our Lord giving the Communion to the apostles; a silver dish of the same date in the Stroganoff Collection at Rome, by some believed to be a paten, has a cross flanked by two angels. Patens with such reliefs long continued to be made in the Eastern Church, as we know from the eleventh- or twelfth-century Byzantine example in the cathedral at Halberstadt in Germany, which has the Crucifixion, with ornamental designs. The Byzantine patens in St. Mark's are of the same sumptuous kind as the chalices which they accompany, and are made of alabaster or agate with metal mounts set with gems, or sometimes with enamelled plaques; one has a central enamel medallion representing Our Lord. On more than one are the words of administration in Greek characters.

We may note that though the circular paten was almost universal other forms seem occasionally to have been used.

An octagonal paten is said in the *Liber Pontificalis*[1] to have been given by Gregory IV to a church in Rome in the ninth century; the gold example accompanying the chalice of Gourdon (p. 107), and decorated with coloured pastes or stones, with a central cross in the same style, is rectangular, following a familiar pagan form of Roman and Hellenistic times. That patens, like chalices, were decorated with gems in the seventh century we learn from passages in the *Liber Pontificalis*.

It will be seen from the above that in the early patens much latitude was allowed in material, subject, and decoration; and in this they may be contrasted with more recent western examples, on which as a rule only the head of Our Lord or the sacred monogram is found. The early paten was also in many cases much larger and more massive than the small and thin patens of the Middle Ages.

Another object used in connexion with the Eucharist, but not often seen, is the strainer (*colum, colatorium*) through which the wine was passed: this instrument, used both in East and West, is recorded as early as the fifth century, and an example of about that time found at Traprain Law in East Lothian has been noted (p. 65). Though the metal tube (*fistula, canna*, etc.) through which bishops or celebrants sometimes communicated appears to have been known as early as the sixth century, no example is known to date from before mediaeval times.

The liturgical fan (*flabellum*, ῥιπίδιον) was used by the deacons to keep flies from the altar. There is abundant evidence of its employment both in the East and in the West; but while the Orthodox Greek Church has retained it to the present day, in the West it was abandoned by the fourteenth century. The Greek *flabellum* is a disk at the end of a straight handle, usually of silver, with ornament of cherubs' heads (cf. fig. 67); two examples of the fourteenth century at Serres in Macedonia are enriched with enamel.

The eucharistic spoon (λαβίς) has been used in the Greek Church from about the tenth century (fig. 69). It is of small size made of gold, silver, or silver-gilt; with it the priest takes from the chalice a fragment of the steeped bread and gives it to the communicant. Liturgical documents make no mention of the use of the spoon in the West, except for placing the bread upon the paten. Spoons with sacred monograms or subjects, in museums and other collections, may in some cases have been

---

[1] The *Liber Pontificalis*, or Papal Chronicle, compiled between A. D. 500 and 880 from Papal archives, makes frequent mention of works of art.

employed for such a purpose as that last mentioned, but there is no evidence of this, and the majority were probably for ordinary use.

The asterisk (lit. star), called by the Copts the dome, is formed of two arched bands of silver at right angles to each other, joined where they cross by a rivet; its purpose is to keep the veil from contact with the bread upon the paten. The asterisk was used in the Byzantine Church in the last centuries of the Empire, but as there is no certain evidence for its employment in early times, it may have been of late introduction; it is said to symbolize the star of Bethlehem, which stood above the place where the young Child lay. It is used by the Greek Church, by the Copts, and by the Catholic Syrians.

Fig. 67.—Coptic flabellum (after Butler).

The Holy Lance, in the form of a small silver spear-head, is used in the Greek Church to divide the bread to be used in the Eucharist. Like the asterisk, it is not known from early times; it has never been adopted in the West.

The pyx for the consecrated bread had various forms. There is evidence that a vessel of precious metal in the shape of a dove was used as early as the fourth century. According to the *Liber Pontificalis*. such a dove was presented by Pope Innocent I to a church in Rome in conjunction with a 'tower' (*turris*, πύργος) and a paten. The tower is mentioned in other places as accompanying the dove, but appears also to have been used alone; it may be assumed to have had a definitely architectural form. By the eleventh century a receptacle for the eucharistic bread of more highly developed architectural type is represented by two examples in the form of domed churches, one in St. Mark's at Venice, the other in the cathedral of Aix-la-Chapelle.

The censer used in Byzantine times was generally either bowl-shaped, with a round foot, or hexagonal with low foot-rim or feet (fig. 68); in both cases it was generally open, though covers sometimes occur. One type of censer had no chains, but was held by a straight handle.

Another object forming part of the usual church furniture was the Gospel Cover by which the book of the Gospels laid upon the altar was protected. Examples of plain silver with the sacred monogram, dating from the fifth or sixth century and found at Luxor, are now in the Cairo Museum. More

Fig. 68.—Silver censer of the sixth century from Cyprus. (No. 399.)

ornate examples were early in use. One, preserved in the Treasury of Monza, made of gold with inlaid garnets, may belong to the time of Gregory the Great. Another, with a cross and borders of massed garnets, is in the Treasury of St. Mark's at Venice, with later examples of about the eleventh century which are enriched with enamels.

Ecclesiastical diptychs of the earlier centuries, used during the Mass at the Commemoration of the names of patriarchs, bishops, and benefactors, living or dead, are now exceedingly rare. As the lists of names were often long, and prayers were sometimes added, large panels were required, and consular diptychs were sometimes appropriated to this use, as in the case of the fine example at Brescia (p. 44), where a diptych of the sixth-century consul Boethius has within, on the sunk surface originally prepared for wax, lists written in ink in the eighth century. The example shown in Wall-Case 5 (fig. 66) was also made to receive wax for writing with a stylus, but the outer sides of the two leaves are quite plain. The lists, which are very long, are written in a Greek hand of the seventh century, and among them are parts of liturgical prayers. The names show that this diptych must have been used either in the diocese of Hermonthis or that of Coptos in Egypt, probably the former, between A. D. 623 and A. D. 662.

Processional crosses are not known with certainty to have been used before the time of Charlemagne, who presented one to Pope Leo III (A. D. 795–816). The only examples in the collection are the remarkable engraved brass crosses from Abyssinia, which show a western influence of a date later than the sixteenth century (plate XV, Wall-Cases 27–30).

In conclusion attention may be drawn to a few less conspicuous or familiar objects of ecclesiastical use. Examples of the thick wooden tablets, placed upon the altars of Abyssinian churches, are shown in Wall-Cases 26–30 (see p. 181). These tablets seem to be related to those let into that part of the upper surface of the Coptic altar on which the elements are placed, though in Egypt the tablet is flush with the surface and concealed from view by the altar cloth. The Coptic tablets are usually engraved with the Greek letters *alpha* and *omega*, and have at the corners the initial and terminal letters of the Greek words: Jesus Christ Son of God ($\overline{\text{IC}}$ $\overline{\text{XC}}$ $\overline{\text{YC}}$ $\overline{\text{ΘY}}$).

In Wall-Cases 29 and 30 is seen one of the thick circular cakes similar in form and in the impressed design to those used for the Eucharist, but not consecrated. Such cakes are distributed among the members of the congregation who have not communicated, and the custom perpetuates an ancient usage in the Christian Church in which portions of unconsecrated bread were distributed in this manner, and described as *Eulogiai* (Gr. εὐλογία, *blessing*). These cakes are stamped with a diaper of crosses, and in the consecrated examples the four central squares are reserved for the priests. Round the edge are generally stamped the Greek words: *Holy is God, holy and mighty, holy and immortal*, though sometimes *Holy, Holy, Holy, Lord God of Hosts* may be substituted (cf. fig. 69).

The metal rattles of the Abyssinian priests, with pierced disks which jingle upon the cross-bars, deserve notice from the resemblance of the type to that of the ancient *sistrum* of Egypt (fig. 104).

The limits of the present Guide do not permit any full description of the vestments worn in the early Church: a few points may however be noticed. Vestments developed out of garments worn in the early centuries of our era (p. 89). The long close-sleeved white under-tunic reaching to the ankles became the *alb*. The upper tunic or *dalmatic*, with shorter and wider sleeves, retained its name, and was the special

Fig. 69.—Coptic Eucharistic bread and spoon (after Butler).

garment of deacons. The *chasuble* was originally an overgarment (*casula, planeta, paenula*), which gradually became ornate, and thus required the addition, out of doors, of the cope (*pluviale, cappa*), originally a kind of poncho: this, as its Latin name implies, served for protection not only against cold, but against rain. Even the episcopal *pallium* descends from an actual garment of the same name, corresponding in the Greek world to the Roman toga. The pallium, at first an ordinary mantle, came to be folded into a narrow form and worn over the *paenula*. For this heavy and manifold band,

I 2

a single strip was ultimately substituted; it was worn over both shoulders, a loop and end hanging to front and back, and was at first fastened by three pins, one of which was on the left shoulder. The final development transformed the long pinned strip into a loop woven in a single piece.

As may be gathered from the origin of vestments in the ordinary garments of Early Christian times, the distinction between the two only grew up gradually, becoming more obvious as secular fashions underwent marked changes, while the conservative usage of the Church retained the old forms. The chief ecclesiastical vestments had approximated to their present form by the sixth century, and down to the ninth there was no great divergence in shape and fashion between East and West; the Greek *sticharion* still corresponds in a general way to the *alb*, the *phenolion* (a word of Greek origin, variously spelled) to the chasuble, and the *omophorion* to the *pallium*.

IV. THE ARTS.[1]

Painting and sculpture. It has been stated above that during the first three centuries of suppression art was symbolic, and chiefly under late Greek influence; the great centre of Hellenistic painting was Alexandria, which inspired both the pagan and the Christian art of Rome. In its late development the Greek manner was naturalistic, retaining little of the idealism of earlier times. Art had derived from oriental sources new principles of ornament and a tendency to luxuriance, but preserved a care for graceful form, and a feeling for restraint in expression; modelling was universal and there was some knowledge of true perspective. This Early Christian symbolic phase is most familiar to us through the mural paintings of the catacombs.

When the early centuries of symbolism were succeeded by a new period of historic and dogmatic expression (p. 27), Greek and Graeco-Roman art retained its importance, not least in the composition of themes and cycles, and in Rome itself influences from the catacombs lasted down to the time of the Gothic wars (p. 28). But it did not satisfy the need of the native populations in Syria, Egypt, and Asia Minor, which shared neither the Greek outlook on the world nor the Greek feeling for restraint and balance. These peoples

[1] The following paragraphs are archaeological and historical only; they do not pretend to aesthetic criticism.

PLATE IX. BYZANTINE SILVER TREASURE FROM CYPRUS.
(*See* p. 173.)

were ready to borrow much from the Greeks and to accept their aid in practical matters, but were determined that the spirit which informed sacred art should be their own. Thus arose a new Christian style composed of Syrian and Hellenistic elements, distinct both from the early Alexandrian symbolism of the catacombs, and from the later secular figure art of Constantinople which continued to reproduce mythological subjects. We saw that this Syro-Hellenistic style was inspired by realism and by a vivid dramatic sense, and that its methods were by no means all Greek. The tendency to use flat colour with little or no modelling, and the suggestion of receding distance by bands or zones one above the other, apparently came to it from Iran, as did some of the ornament which it employed, such as formal scrolls and diapers, and conventional animals or monsters. Inverted perspective (p. 20), the frontal position, and the representation of divine figures in majesty, like the great kings of the ancient monarchies, were all of Syrian and Mesopotamian origin. This Syro-Hellenistic sacred art, representing a compromise between the Semitic and the Greek points of view, became general after the fifth century alike in East and West, the Syrian element predominating in work produced under monastic influence, the Hellenistic still strongly asserted in cities like Alexandria, Antioch, and Constantinople, where for one reason or another Greek influences were powerful. In a country like Egypt, where a great Hellenistic city stood on the coast, while a short way up the Nile valley the population was Coptic, we can follow a progressive increase of the native feeling at the expense of the Greek. Even in the single example of mural painting in the collection, that from Wadi Sarga (Wall-Cases 16 and 17), the small inset with the Three Children in the burning fiery furnace (fig. 70) is nearer to the Hellenistic manner than the large figures of SS. Cosmas and Damian, where we note characterization and preoccupation with details. In the extensive wall paintings of Bawît and in other work of the fifth and sixth centuries it is possible to trace the changing relation of Alexandrian and native elements. But in all Christian countries a similar interaction may be remarked; in some of the mosaics at Ravenna, for instance in the procession of Saints in the nave of St. Apollinare Nuovo, Hellenistic feeling is strong; in the ceremonial scenes in St. Vitale in the same city, representing Justinian and Theodora with their suites, the eastern influence predominates.

In the period between the seventh and the tenth centuries

representational sacred art was threatened at the same time by iconoclasm and by Persian decorative art (p. 41), and on the monumental scale little now remains. But in Constantinople iconoclasm was indirectly favourable to a secular Hellenistic art and to a general strengthening of Greek influence (p. 50). After the restoration of pictures, this influence was reflected in religious art, which in the tenth century shows, in the capital at least, an accentuation of the

Fig. 70.—Wall painting from Wadi Sarga: the Three Children in the furnace, with Coptic inscription: sixth century.

Hellenistic as compared with the Syrian element. But in monastic centres like Cappadocia, this was not the case, and even in Constantinople, as time went on, the oriental element was reasserted under the monastic influence which, under the leadership of the Monastery of the Studium, had won the battle for orthodoxy against the enemies of pictures (p. 50). Thus from the eleventh century to the Latin occupation of A. D. 1204 the Syro-Hellenistic style again prevailed, if in a modified form, Greek or oriental factors advancing or receding according as Court or monastic influences prevailed. In the mosaics of Daphni in Attica, for instance, the Greek factor is more in evidence than in those in the great church of St. Luke of Stiris in Phocis, a fact which may possibly be explained by Court patronage in the former case; the mosaic of the Last Judgement at the West End of the Cathedral of Torcello, on the other hand, conspicuously illustrates the oriental methods of inverted perspective and vertical projection (p. 20). The illumination of manuscripts is throughout of the greatest interest and importance for the illustration of these changes and developments in sacred art; here the Hellenistic style of the Court and the eastern tendencies of monastic art can most conveniently be studied (see below). Ornament in this period grew, as a whole, uncompromisingly oriental. Floral scrolls and repeating designs, with conventionalized animal motives, form the substance of decoration. Nearly all this work was of Iranian origin, and the beasts in their formal character and arrangement contrast strongly with the naturalistic types of the early years when Hellenistic influences were still strong.

During the Latin interregnum at Constantinople painting and other arts in the capital were rudely interrupted. But the intercourse with the West, notably with Italy, which took place in the thirteenth century had interesting effects upon East Christian art; Byzantine painting, by contact with the rising art of Siena, gained somewhat in freedom and grace, while retaining unaltered its fundamentally eastern character. This is apparent in mural paintings in the churches of Serbia, a country in the thirteenth and fourteenth centuries under strong native rulers, where many Byzantine artists at this time received patronage and were able to train a native Serbian school. It is also apparent in the small religious pictures in tempera on wooden panels, the work of Greek painters who from Venice extended their activities through northern Italy. But if these immigrants into Italy received much, they probably gave even more, since their technical knowledge and their tradition were of great service to the first Sienese painters, whose work, even down to the time of Duccio, shows sufficient signs of Byzantine influence. With the fourteenth century, panel-painters connected with Crete and Venice formed a school known as the Cretan school, which lasted for several hundred years, surviving the fall of the Byzantine Empire; to its later periods belong many small panel pictures of the sixteenth and seventeenth centuries, often erroneously described as Byzantine. The Cretan School was not confined to painters of ikons, but produced a succession of mural painters, whose style recalls that of the artist familiar with a smaller scale; it succeeded an earlier or Macedonian school perhaps originally based upon Salonika, the members of which worked in a broader manner. The greater part of the frescoes upon Mount Athos, dating from the sixteenth century and later, belong to the Cretan School.

Fig. 71.—Head-piece from an eleventh-century Byzantine MS. in the British Museum (Harley 5785).

After the restoration of Greek rule at Constantinople towards the close of the thirteenth century, painting was affected by the general unsettlement (p. 53). It was a time in which artists, no longer brought up in a sound tradition, were thrown upon their own resources, and imitated religious and secular works of preceding centuries without always understanding their several styles. In single subjects they could produce pleasing results; the absence of training is betrayed when details and methods borrowed from sources differing in style are united in a single composition, as in the mosaics of Kahrieh Jami (the old Church of the Chora) at Constantinople, where Hellenistic true perspective and oriental inverted perspective (p. 20) are found together in the same subject, the incongruity marring the picturesque and animated effect of the whole. But in a sense the very want of the old discipline lends a certain freshness and brightness to much work of the time; and perhaps the revival of art fared better than the contemporary revival in literature, since to a certain extent it had been enriched by contact with Italian culture. The most coherent work upon the larger scale is perhaps to be sought not in the capital but in the province of Mistra in the Morea (p. 54) and in the Balkans.

A very few words may be added upon technical methods. East Christian and Byzantine painting is almost always in tempera. Upon walls the colours were applied to plaster already dry, and a medium was employed, in the form of size, gum, or white of egg; true fresco, if used at all, was extremely rare. In the case of panels, a thin layer of fine plaster was first applied to the wood, and upon this the subject was painted; the plaster can be seen in the damaged parts of the thirteenth-century panels from Egypt in Wall-Case 6. Encaustic painting upon panels with hot wax applied by metal spatulae, the method employed in the late-Egyptian portraits of the Fayûm, survived into Christian times; a few panels of the sixth century and later, obtained on Mount Sinai, are preserved at Kieff. In mosaic, cubes (*tesserae*) were fixed in cement applied to a base of stone or brick. In the case of pavements they were generally of marble or other stone, and of brick; in the case of wall-decoration they were almost all of coloured glass; the cubes with gold are of plain glass with a piece of gold foil upon one face, covered by a protecting film of clear glass, as in the case of the larger 'gilded glasses' of the catacombs (p 140). The expense and labour of covering the upper walls, vaults, and domes of a whole church was very great, and it is easy to understand that the practice fell into disuse when the Byzantine Empire grew poor. A calculation made in connection with mosaic decoration of the church of St. George at Salonika showed that thirty-six million *tesserae* must have been used for the dome alone, and each had to be independently fixed in place. Small panel-pictures in mosaic were made in some numbers between the tenth and twelfth centuries, probably at Constantinople. Here the base is of wax applied to the wooden surface, and in this minute cubes of glass, stone, gold, etc., are fixed. An example is to be seen in the Victoria and Albert Museum.

As indicated above, the destinies of manuscript-illumination obeyed the same general influences which controlled the growth of mural painting and mosaic. In the first centuries manuscripts in the form of rolls in a purely Hellenistic style provided themes and cycles from which the oriental illuminators had much to learn. Some of the first books (*codices*) were also classical in style; the fragments of the Cotton Genesis in the British Museum afford a valuable example. With the fifth century probably began the production in the monasteries of illuminated books under oriental (chiefly Syrian) influences. Famous examples of the sixth and seventh centuries survive, among which may once more be mentioned the Gospels of the Syrian monk Rabula, in Florence, painted at Zagba in northern Mesopotamia in A.D. 586, the Gospels at Edgmiatsin in Armenia, also of Syrian origin, and those at Rossano in Italy, probably produced in Cappadocia. We have seen how much was done by books of this kind, transported by travelling monks and traders, to inspire the earliest mediaeval painters of the West. Whether they were themselves illuminators, or worked on the greater scale on church walls, their influence is discerned in the first illuminations of the Italians and the Franks; and in the figure subjects of early Celtic books, such as the Lindisfarne Gospels (p. 68); it was manifest in early German books, and in short was a general source of inspiration throughout the West. East Christian and Byzantine illuminated books are represented in the collections of the Department of Manuscripts, and examples, chiefly of the Middle Byzantine period, are exhibited in the Grenville Library (opening out of the Entrance Hall), Case 1.

We may resume the main points in the foregoing paragraphs.

Beginning under late-Hellenistic auspices, Christian painting became orientalized after the Peace of the Church under influences which were principally Semitic (Syrian); the result was a sacred art, described as Syro-Hellenistic, in which a compromise was effected between Greek and eastern elements. In the Byzantine capital, the iconoclasm of the eighth and ninth centuries led to a certain revulsion in favour of Hellenism, but at the same time to a fresh wave of Asiatic ornament. But the monastic influences which during the bitter struggle had at last worn down the attack upon sacred pictures were now reasserted, and held their own until the Fourth Crusade of A.D. 1204. The Latin interregnum of about sixty years

THE ARTS

broke the tradition of the schools in the capital, and many painters went abroad. Art came back with the Restoration freer, and to a greater extent in the hands of laymen, but without the old consistent discipline. It developed an almost feverish activity, copying early models of diverse origin; but the general impoverishment and the disaster of A.D. 1453 prevented a healthy growth; thus Byzantine painting did not end, as is commonly supposed, in hieratic stiffness, but rather in a certain rashness of experiment. It may be added that in the countries of the Orthodox Greek Church, religious painting in the Byzantine manner has continued to our own day, often little affected by a contemporary secular art inspired by that of western Europe.

Sculpture in its turn was exposed to general influences similar to those which affected painting. The figure art of the earlier Christian centuries was almost entirely in Greek hands. The Hellenistic cities were the sources which inspired both Rome and Constantinople; Asia Minor seems to have possessed the chief centres of production; here the tradition of antique sculpture survived in greater purity, and marble was accessible. The early sarcophagi with high relief, and other examples of marble with figure-sculpture, are of Greek tradition, whether found in Italy, Spain, or the south of France. The ceremonial or historical reliefs of the fourth and fifth centuries upon the shafts or plinths of columns, upon arches, or the bases of obelisks at Constantinople, recall earlier Roman work produced under similar conditions, but are less accomplished. Among the oriental Christian peoples only the Copts showed

FIG. 72.—Coptic decorative sculpture: sixth century.

a certain taste for figure-sculpture of Hellenistic suggestion, chiefly applied to the decoration of buildings, using the readily-worked limestone of the Nile Valley; their work has often a pronounced realistic tendency. Syria produced no independent major sculpture. After the time of Justinian figure sculpture on the large scale declined, though statues of emperors were made down to about the seventh century. Reliefs, however, survived iconoclasm, and throughout the

Fig. 73.—Coptic decorative sculpture from Wadi Sarga: sixth century.

later periods Our Lord, the Virgin, and saints continued to be represented; but the influence of sculpture was never comparable in extent or in emotional appeal to that of painting. The West as a whole was not distinguished for figure sculpture between the fall of the Roman Empire and the Romanesque period. The Lombard reliefs are of a rude character; the Franks, skilled in ivory carving, where they followed East Christian models, did not practise the greater art. After

THE ARTS

the time of the Northumbrian crosses (p. 66), we have remarkable hunting-reliefs upon the upright stones of Scotland, but here religious subjects are few. The next serious effort in this field in Britain was made in the South of England, where the reliefs of the tenth and eleventh centuries at Chichester, Bradford-on-Avon, and Romsey show affinity to the illuminated MSS. of the Winchester School. On the continent the revival of sculpture began in the eleventh century, partly through the inspiration of Byzantine ivory carvings.

On the smaller scale, sculpture shows more vitality, especially in the case of ivory carvings; in these alone did Syro-Hellen-

FIG. 74.—Coptic limestone capital: sixth century.

istic sacred art find sculptural expression. Ivory carvings like the panels upon the chair of Maximianus at Ravenna, or the large book-covers, have their full share in the historical and didactic expression of the time; and while some retain Greek traditions with remarkable purity, others have obvious oriental qualities in which the respective shares of Egypt and Syria are hard to disentangle.

In the centuries after iconoclasm ivory carving, now practised chiefly in the capital, reached its highest point in the tenth and eleventh centuries; it was particularly susceptible to the classical influences which prevailed in a society brought up upon Greek literature. Most ivories were now made for purely devotional purposes, and in these objects the last phase of Hellenism became intimately expressive of religious feeling. Their merit and their portability combined to make them, as already noted, effective agents in the revival of western art, when monumental sculpture in stone aspired once more

Fig. 75.—Marble slab, carved on both sides, from Miafarqin: twelfth century.

to its rightful place (p. 51). The evidence of a fine tradition in the figures on the seventh-century high crosses of Ruthwell in Dumfriesshire and Bewcastle in Cumberland (p. 66) suggests a similar service rendered by ivories of an earlier time; these reliefs, appearing in an age when larger sculpture had sunk to a low level, are difficult to explain except on some such theory.

Stone sculpture in the Christian East found its most characteristic expression not in figure-carving but in decoration. This ornament, chiefly devoted to the enrichment of buildings, was early developed; with the fifth century, the Hellenistic treatment of palmette and acanthus in high relief, though never wholly superseded, in most places gave way to a decoration in a single plane, in which a more highly conventionalized foliage, now including that of the vine, was treated as if it were textile ornament, the primary inspiration probably coming from Persia and Central Asia. The pattern was usually relieved against black shadow by deeply cutting away the background (cf. fig. 72), or sometimes, as in the case of closure-slabs, by piercing; occasionally the ground of a design cut in flat and low relief was filled in with a dark mastic, to produce a similar effect. The marble quarries on the island of Proconnesos in the Sea of Marmora became a great centre of export for richly carved capitals which were sent as far west as North Africa and Spain. After iconoclasm and the Arab wars, a conventionalized beast-ornament of Perso-Mesopotamian origin was added to the foliate designs of earlier times; but this too was treated on similar principles. The animals were not naturalistic, as in the early centuries under Hellenistic influence, but used merely as ornament, and carved in flat relief. This decorative sculpture, both floral and animal, served primarily to enrich architecture, and is found on capitals, closure-slabs and window-slabs (cf. fig. 75), lintels and tympana. The greater part of all this ornament seems also to have owed its inspiration to Persia, and the relation of the later designs to those of Mohammedan art has already been noticed (p. 43). In Egypt there was an admirable development of decorative sculpture, through which imported motives in time assumed a local character.

Minor Arts.

Silversmith's work. The earliest Christians belonged to various classes of the community. As their number grew, they soon included wealthy persons accustomed to silver plate and still enjoying such luxuries of their pagan neighbours as they considered harmless. During the time of persecution, there were few valuable church utensils, and silver was confined to personal use; in the Esquiline Treasure (Wall-Cases 9 and 10) the

Museum possesses a remarkable example of such plate (p. 174), with the sacred monogram and a Christian inscription connecting it with the wedding of two members of Roman families. The great hoard of broken silver vessels discovered at Traprain Law in East Lothian (p. 65) in 1919, and now in the Royal Scottish Museum at Edinburgh, the most remarkable discovery of the kind made in the British Islands, includes several objects with affinities in form or ornament to the Esquiline Treasure; among these is a cylindrical toilet-box resembling those filling the domed casket in Wall-Case 10. The Traprain Treasure, probably the spoils of a Saxon raid, is of great interest for the study of Early Christian art, since a vase included in it has Scriptural subjects in relief—Adam and Eve, and the Adoration of the Magi. Like the Esquiline Treasure it appears to date from about A.D. 400; some

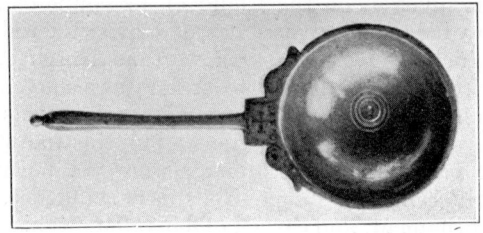

Fig 76.—Silver spoon with cross in niello, from the Carthage Treasure: early fifth century. (No. 364.)

silver basins with beaded edges bring it also into relation with the treasure from Carthage in the present collection (Wall-Case 12 and p. 175). The lost silver vessel of the period of the Roman occupation of Britain, from Corbridge in Northumberland (p. 65), should be mentioned in connexion with these other early examples, as also the pewter service from Appleshaw in Hampshire mentioned on p. 66.

Since the Greek craftsmen of the Mediterranean cities led the way in the arts of luxury, which indeed were introduced by them into Rome, it is natural that early silver should bear a Hellenistic or Graeco-Roman character. As in the case of other branches of art, this is most noticeable in the oldest examples; in course of time, though a classical influence persisted, other influences of oriental origin lent the work a distinctive style. A larger proportion of the plate dating from the period after the fourth century has been found in the nearer East, chiefly in Syria, Egypt, and Cyprus, and most of it seems to have belonged to monasteries or churches rather than to private persons. It is often difficult to decide whether the work in a particular case should be ascribed to Alexandria or Antioch, which were probably the great centres of production. Possibly in the sixth century Syrian plate was the more widely distributed; rather numerous examples found in the east of Russia, where they were traded for furs, appear also to have Syrian relationships. Apart from ornament in relief, this silver plate is enriched with designs in niello, and from the fifth century has frequently Byzantine control-marks on the back, which may perhaps be regarded as the earliest 'hall-marks' in existence (fig. 77). The collection contains one silver cup which is certainly a chalice (fig. 65

Fig 77.—Stamps on the base of the silver censer, fig. 68.

Fig. 77 a.—Monogram and inscription on spoon of the sixth century, Lampsacus treasure. (No. 390.)

and p. 108), and another, in the Lampsacus Treasure, of unusual form, but possibly also made for sacramental use: both date from the sixth century. With the Lampsacus cup are two shallow bowls which may have served as patens (p. 110). Christian silver plate later than the seventh century has not been preserved to the same extent as that of earlier times, partly as a result of the Arab and Turkish conquests. The occupation of Constantinople by the Crusaders at the beginning of the thirteenth century was the indirect cause of preserving for us many objects, carried off to the West and now among Church treasures, which might not otherwise have come down to our times; on the other hand, the general plunder of the churches by these same crusaders led to the destruction of precious objects in even larger numbers. The combination of enamel with ecclesiastical silver work in the Christian East calls for some notice. Where it is found, as on chalices and patens in St. Mark's at Venice, it is not embedded in the substance of the object, as is generally the case where it is employed in western mediaeval art; separate enamelled plaques are applied to the surface, and in some cases bordered with pearls.

In the Christian East, as in the West, goldsmith's work was naturally employed on a great scale in the service of ecclesiastical art. Apart from objects used in churches, and the plate already described (pp. 106 ff.), we may note that altar-frontals and iconostases were enriched with work in the precious metals and in bronze; these, with reliquaries, candle-sticks, crosses, and other objects were produced in fine workmanship from quite early times down to the fifteenth century, and continue to be made in the countries of the Orthodox Greek Church. Since these things are scantily represented in British collections, only a few general remarks can be made upon them here.

As in the West, architectural forms controlled the structure and decoration of many objects; thus the *artophorion* for consecrated bread might take the form of a domed church, and is thus as closely connected with ecclesiastical architecture as Gothic reliquaries in the West. But in the East forms changed less frequently than in the West, so that the constant variety in the types of canopies, traceries, and pinnacles which diversifies western designs and makes them comparatively easy to date is not to be found in oriental work.

Jewellery and goldsmith's work. The jewellery, like the plate, used by Christians could at first only be distinguished from contemporary pagan ornaments by the presence of Christian symbols, such as we find, for example, on early rings; in its general aspect, it shared the characteristics of the Graeco-Roman goldsmith's art. In the first few centuries, while Hellenistic influence was strong, modelling was still found, but, as in the case of decorative sculpture, pierced work rapidly gained in favour. As this method produced its best effect on an extended surface, it was one cause of a general tendency toward fragility. The jeweller aimed at superficial display; and the work of the period between the fourth and seventh centuries is apt to have more splendour and less solidity than that of earlier times. The stones chiefly used were root of emerald (plasma) and sapphire, both of large size, and polished, but not faceted. The favourite colour-scheme is therefore blue, green, and gold; and since the pierced work, with its contrast of light and shadow, also produces effects of colour,

PLATE X. GILDED GLASSES: OUR LORD, AND A FAMILY GROUP.

this late jewellery diverges both in purpose and result from that of the ancient Greeks, who considered above all fine finish, form, and proportion. The stones were often made to alternate with pearls threaded on gold wires, by means of which the general richness was enhanced; rows of pearls, threaded on gold wire passing at intervals through gold loops, were used to frame different sections. The method of enriching gold ornaments by a kind of mosaic of garnets or glass pastes (*orfévrerie cloisonnée*, ' inlaid jewellery '), introduced from the East as early as the fourth century and common to Byzantine and early Teutonic goldsmiths, is less known in the Christian East through actual jewellery than through such objects as Gospel covers and reliquaries. The finest examples are in the Treasury of St. Mark's at Venice, and in the cathedral at Limburg-on-the-Lahn, in Germany; the oldest at present known is the reliquary at Poitiers, dating from the sixth century (pp. 145, 147).

Jewellery has survived in greater quantities from the period between the fourth and seventh centuries than from subsequent times. Like silver plate, in association with which it has been often found, it has come to light in various parts of the Christian East, but notably in Egypt, Syria, and Cyprus. The tendency to display is often redeemed by the fine quality of the pierced work, and by the pleasant harmony of the colours. Enamel (p. 145) was employed at least as early as the sixth century (cf. ear-rings in Table-Case B), but is not common on jewellery; motives are also inlaid in niello. The sumptuousness of the ornaments worn by imperial persons is illustrated by miniatures in illuminated MSS., and by such mosaics as those in St. Vitale at Ravenna, showing the Emperor and Empress with their suites. Crowns or tiaras had large pendants of pearls, and pearls were also sewn to the imperial robes. Though not so well represented by surviving examples, the middle Byzantine period was also rich in personal ornaments (see the rings and other small ornaments in Table-Cases A and B), though the size of individual objects appears to have been reduced. At all periods gems were mounted in plain raised settings.

The principal forms in use were collars and necklaces, ear-rings, bracelets, and finger rings. Brooches, though worn, are not frequently found; in both the above-mentioned periods pectoral crosses and small reliquaries were suspended on chains from the neck. Among exceptional objects may be mentioned parts of regalia, such as the crown at Budapest sent in the

132   INTRODUCTION

eleventh century by the Emperor Constantine Monomachos to a Hungarian king, where enamelled plaques form the principal feature of the decoration.

Ear-rings were often large and heavy, with pendants of gems and pearls; others were crescent-shaped (lunate), usually with pierced designs: examples of both kinds are exhibited.

Fig. 78.—Pierced gold disk; centre-piece from an ornament of chains to cover breast and back: Egypt: sixth century.

Large gold collars or gorgets were worn in the earlier period, sometimes formed of a series of finely pierced plaques set with gems, sometimes tubular, having a kind of gorget which framed and supported a number of gold coins and medallions: possibly the latter type, which is unduly heavy in appearance, may have been worn as a mark of rank or office. Necklaces were of chain with frequent gems at intervals,

THE ARTS 133

and sometimes with a line of pendants hanging from the front. The collection contains an unusual ornament in the shape of an arrangement of chains formed of pierced disks, intended to cover both breast and back, a larger disk occupying the central position in each case (p. 186 and fig. 78).

Bracelets were often broad and flat, with pierced designs and a medallion opening and closing by means of a hinge and clasp (fig. 81 and Table-Case B). In some cases the whole

Fig. 79.—Byzantine gold pectoral cross with inscription (Galatians iv. 14) in niello. (No. 285.)

Fig. 80.—Byzantine gold pectoral cross. (No. 287.)

exterior of a flat bracelet, band and medallion alike, was covered with gems and pearls; in others the band was formed of a rich scroll of vine or other foliage in openwork.

The class of finger-rings is exceptionally important, since it includes examples from very early times, some of those with intaglio gems coming from the Roman Catacombs; moreover the ring served other purposes than mere ornament, being used as a sign of betrothal or marriage and as a signet. Rings as signets or ornaments were as widely spread among the early Christians as among their pagan contemporaries. St. James (Ep. ii. 2) speaks of the man who wears a gold ring and goodly apparel, and the Fathers of the Church were obliged to reprimand the community for extravagance in this respect. Tertullian condemns the prodigal use of rings, and Clement of Alexandria also condemns extravagance, adding a few interesting details as to the manner in which Christians should wear their rings, and the subjects which they ought to choose. The ring, he says, should be placed on the little finger as low down as possible, and the devices should be taken from the primitive symbolic subjects, such as the dove, fish, ship, or anchor. As might be expected, the engraved stones mounted in the rings have come down to us in greater numbers than the metal rings themselves, and the visitor should notice that a large number of the examples in the case have been remounted in comparatively modern times. The earliest Christian gems are all engraved in *intaglio*, which means that the device is hollowed below the surface of the stone; cameo stones, with subjects cut in relief, are rarer, and usually later than the first two or three centuries. The stones most frequently employed are carnelian, sard, garnet, varieties of onyx (including the combination of blue and black layers usually known as *nicolo*), jasper, and chalcedony; more valuable stones such as emerald and sapphire occur less frequently. The quality of the engraved work compared with that of the classical period is generally poor, and some of it is exceedingly rough.

Designs were also engraved upon the metal of which the ring was composed, and this procedure, which was far easier for the workman, became very common in the later centuries. A ring was a favourite form of gift, and the inscriptions upon Early Christian rings frequently take the form of acclamations, or expressions of good will, praying for the piety and prosperity of the recipient, whose name is sometimes but not always mentioned. The commonest acclamation is *vivas in Deo*, 'may'st thou live in God'.

Rings played a prominent part in connexion with marriage from the earliest Christian times, and had been similarly used both among the Romans and the Jews. The ring was placed on the bride's finger, not, as among ourselves, in the course of the marriage ceremony, but during the previous betrothal in her father's house. The outward signs of the entry into the married state were rather the veil, which, after

the first two centuries, was actually assumed during the
ceremony, and the crowns of gold, silver, green leaves, or
flowers, which both bride and bridegroom wore, and which
were returned to the church after the lapse of seven days.
Marriage-crowns, which were used both by Jews and pagans
in pre-Christian times, are still in use in many countries;
and in the Eastern Church they are kept upon the altar,
being placed on the heads of the bride and bridegroom after

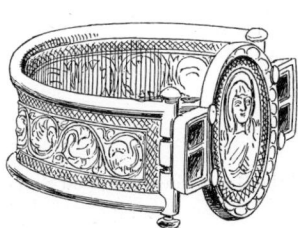

Fig. 81.—Gold bracelet: sixth century. (No 279.)

Fig. 82.—Gold signet-ring: perhaps of the fifth century. (No. 190.)

Fig. 83.—Gold signet-ring: seventh century. (No. 189.)

Fig. 84.—Silver signet-ring worn as an amulet. (No. 142.)

the benediction. One of the gilded glasses (No. 613) should
be noticed in connexion with the custom of crowning, for here
Our Lord is Himself seen holding the wreaths. On three
Byzantine rings (Nos. 130, 131, and 132) Our Lord extends
His hands over the heads of the bride and bridegroom, or
places them on their shoulders, the attitude evidently signifying an act of benediction. In No. 129 Our Lord blesses
only the bridegroom, while the Virgin lays her hand upon

the bride. No. 49 (fig. 30) may have been a betrothal ring, and in examples like No. 207 (fig. 31), where a male and female bust are seen together, such a destination may certainly be assumed.

Engraved gems, seals, and coins. The intaglio gem, at first

Fig. 85.—Engraved gem : fourth century : the Good Shepherd, and Story of Jonah. (No 25.)

much used in rings, seems to have gone out of favour in the later periods, and such gems as have come down to us

Fig. 86.—Onyx Cameo: the Annunciation : ninth century. (No. 104.)

Fig. 87.—Heliotrope Cameo : Our Lord. (No. 106.)

from the eighth century and later are usually cameos on onyx, or reliefs of cameo size in heliotrope (bloodstone), and softer stone like steatite : the last-mentioned stone was also used for yet larger reliefs on the scale of ivory carvings. East-Christian gems seldom reach a high level, and this branch of art seems to have been much neglected; the best cameos date from the tenth and eleventh centuries.

Documents in the Christian East were sealed during the Middle Ages by means of leaden *bullae* pierced to receive the cords on which they were suspended. Like the bullae and pendent wax seals of the Middle Ages in the West, they had a design on each face impressed by a matrix; the signet-ring, therefore, largely went out of use, not being adapted for impressing lead. It is a singular thing that while a very large number of matrices, chiefly in bronze, have come down from the mediaeval centuries in the West, not half a dozen have been found in the East; yet even if iron was the metal used it might have been expected that many would have survived intact. The designs on Byzantine lead impressions are generally figures of Our Lord, the Virgin, and saints; very often one side is covered by the legend or inscription. The collection of such lead impressions is in the Department of Manuscripts.

The coins of the Byzantine Empire have a certain monotony, and are less finely modelled than those of classical antiquity. In the later centuries they are often rudely designed and badly minted, producing almost an effect of barbarism. Yet by the conventions which they observe, the best designers often attain results both appropriate and satisfactory, comparing favourably with much work of our own day. Coins were struck in gold, silver, and bronze. The obverse of the Byzantine coin usually bore the bust or full figure of the Emperor, sometimes associated with members of his family, or, more rarely, with figures of Our Lord or the Virgin placing the crown on his head. There is greater variety in the case of the reverse. The Victories or Fortunes of the early centuries were replaced at the end of the sixth century by a cross standing on steps, a design of long duration. The bust of Our Lord is seen on the reverse for the first time on coins of Justinian II at the close of the seventh century; and, after the interval caused by iconoclasm, again in the ninth century. At this time an enthroned type was introduced, which long continued in use. The Virgin is first seen on a reverse in coins of Leo VI (A.D. 886–912); and the first saint to occupy this position, St. Alexander, in the reign of the emperor of that name (A.D. 912–13). The portrait upon Byzantine coins is conventional; from the sixth century the profile is abandoned, and only the facing head employed. The chief gold coin was the *solidus* or *nomisma*, weighing about 70 grains; a half-solidus or *semissis* and a third-solidus or *tremissis* were issued down to the tenth century. The collection of Byzantine coins is in the Department of Coins and Medals.

Bronze money-weights or *exagia*, used for weighing coins,

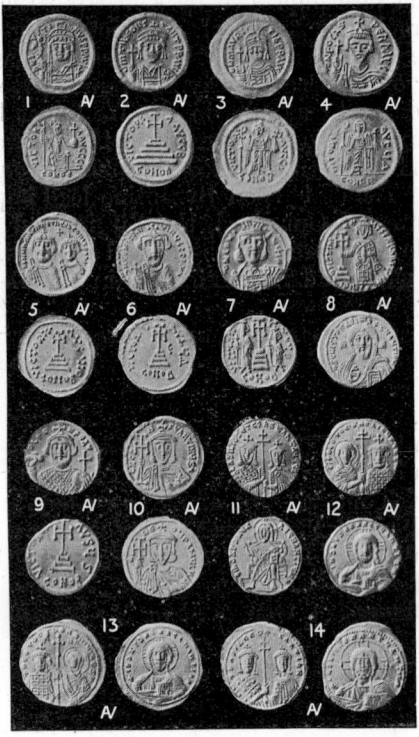

Fig. 88.—Byzantine coins: Justin II (A.D. 565-578) to Basil II (A.D. 976-1025.)

are exhibited in Table-Case A; the denominations, usually inlaid with silver, are accompanied by busts of emperors or officials; more rarely, as in the largest example shown, by figures of saints. The larger weights were for weighing numbers of coins, seventy-two *solidi* making a pound. The letters S. or N. stand for *solidus* or *nomisma*. The letters ⌐ are the abbreviation for the ounce (οὐγκία) of six *solidi*. The characters used are both Greek and Latin, the weights dating from a time when Latin was still used for official purposes in the Eastern Empire. Most of the examples come from the Byzantine provinces, and sometimes have upon them the names of prefects and officials controlling the standards of weights and measures, as is the case with Nos. 433, 435, and 436. Occasionally (as in No. 447), imperial busts occur; and on No. 444 is the name of Theodoric, showing that these weights were used in the Gothic dominions of Northern Italy. Occa-

Fig. 89.—Byzantine bronze pound-weight, with two military saints inlaid in silver: sixth century. (No. 483.)

sionally the surface is elaborately decorated, and in the fine pound weight No. 483 (fig. 89) two military saints are represented.

Flat circular glass weights (Nos. 660-85) were used in the Byzantine Empire in the sixth century for weighing coins. They are usually stamped on one side with a bust or monogram accompanied by the name of an Eparch or provincial governor. The majority come from Egypt and Syria.

Glass. The glass vessels used by Christians must in general have had the same forms, and have been made in the same manner as that of their pagan contemporaries, examples of which are to be seen in the King Edward VII Gallery. The plain glass vessels obtained in such numbers from tombs at Nazareth have no obvious Christian associations, but many are of a kind which may have been used by Christians.

The glass industry rose to importance in Hellenistic times, and its chief centres appear to have been Alexandria and the cities of the Phoenician coast, whence it passed into Rome in imperial times. Most of the glass for ordinary use was blown, and examples of cups, bottles, etc., dating from the third and fourth centuries, have been found in Egypt. We need only differentiate Christian from ordinary Roman glass when it has a religious decoration, and here the two most important classes are engraved glass and the so-called gilded glass of the Roman catacombs. In the former, Christian subjects are cut with the wheel, usually in rather rough fashion; the collection contains an example from Cologne (No. 652) with biblical subjects (Wall-Case 6).

Fig. 90.—Byzantine bronze money-weight: sixth century. (No. 453.)

The gilded glasses (Pl. X and XI) are so well represented in the collection that they must be noticed at greater length. They date from the third to the fifth century, and are often described by the Italian name *fondi d'oro* (gilded bases) from the fact that the majority are actually the bottoms of drinking vessels from which the upper parts have been broken away. Some of these vessels were shallow saucer-shaped bowls, others more nearly resembled tumblers; the great majority were made for domestic use, and, as the inscriptions show, given away as presents, probably on the occasion of weddings, birthdays, and other anniversaries. It is possible that here and there an exceptional specimen may have been used in the celebration of the Eucharist; such a use has in fact been proposed for the bowl No. 629, which has been held by some to be a paten. But there is no conclusive evidence that any of the specimens now preserved were made for a liturgical purpose, and the earliest known forms of chalice (p. 106) differ from that of any of the gilded glasses. Nor is it now considered likely that these glasses as a group were made for the *Agape* or love-feasts of the primitive Christians, because very many of them date from a period when the love-feast in its primitive form had been discontinued. The most generally accepted theory is that the greater part are purely domestic, but that some, especially those with figures of particular saints, may have been used at the commemorative feasts held at the tombs

Fig. 91.—Glass disk ('gilded glass') with scriptural subjects, found at Cologne: fourth century. (No. 628.)

Subjects reading from the top round to the left: two scenes from the story of Jonah, Daniel in the lions' den, the Three Children of Babylon in the fiery furnace, the Healing of the young man born blind, the Widow of Nain, the Healing of the Paralytic, and the Dream of Ezekiel. In the centre: part of the scene of the Good Shepherd (?).

of the apostles and martyrs during the fourth and early fifth centuries. In favour of this view, it may be mentioned that the treatment of many specimens is secular and sometimes pagan, so that the glasses cannot have been collectively designed for a religious use. De Rossi has shown that it was a custom among the Early Christians to impress in the mortar of the freshly-closed *loculi* (see p. 72) in the catacombs all kinds of small objects, such as ivory plaques, combs, toys, beads, coins, cubes of mosaic, and even twigs. The object was to identify individual graves, for the name of the deceased was not always placed upon the front of his tomb, and even if it was, the objects adhering to the plaster made recognition easier. Some of these may have been possessions of the deceased during life; but many would appear to have been left behind by friends and relatives who had been present at the interment. Gilded glasses have been found under the same conditions, and may thus have served the same purpose. They have hardly ever been discovered in a perfect state, and their upper parts may either have been destroyed by accident or else deliberately broken off in order that they might not project into the narrow space of the subterranean corridors. Their disappearance is of less moment, as the designs and inscriptions were almost always in the bottoms of the vessels. Some of the disks with smoothly ground edges probably never formed part of vessels at all, but are thought to have been made simply as medallions. In addition to the pagan subjects already mentioned, which are few in number, the favourite designs are portraits of husbands and wives, with or without their children, and figures of saints, usually with their names appended. Especially popular were representations of St. Peter and St. Paul, who are seen, for example, on No. 636 in the collection. The most usual inscription, in addition to the ordinary acclamation *vivas*, 'may'st thou live', and its amplifications, is *pie zeses*, a Latin form of the Greek words πίε ζήσαις, 'drink and live, i. e. drink and good health to thee'.

The *fondi d'oro* usually consist of two layers of glass. To one of these is gummed a sheet of gold leaf on which the design is etched with a needle, and a protecting layer of glass is then welded on by subjecting the whole to the action of heat. The old Roman glass, which was produced by wood fires, probably cohered at a low temperature, and the use of powdered glass (flux) between the layers may not have been as necessary as it would be in the case of ordinary modern glass. If the design was applied to a completed bowl it was

PLATE XI. GILDED GLASSES DANIEL AND THE DRAGON; A GLADIATOR.
(*See* p. 186.)

perhaps etched directly on foil already applied to the bottom; when the etching was finished, the protecting glass was laid over it, and the bowl was placed in the oven face downwards until cohesion took place. Some have suggested, however, that the protecting layer was formed by blowing a film of molten glass over the surface. Whatever the exact method may have been, the style of ornamentation by means of gold foil between two layers of glass is probably of Egyptian origin, as examples of similar work connected with that country are in existence which are older than any of the catacomb glasses; among these may be mentioned two glass bowls found at Canosa in South Italy, but probably made in Alexandria, exhibited in the King Edward VII Gallery. The process was still known, by tradition at least, in the Early Middle Ages, and was again practised for small pictures or panels in Italy in the fourteenth century. Pictures etched in gold foil on glass, though without a second protecting layer, were made in still later times, and in Bohemia tumblers with designs enclosed between two layers were produced in the eighteenth century. More recently reproductions in the old style of the Catacomb glasses have been attempted, though the effect is seldom equal to that of the original.

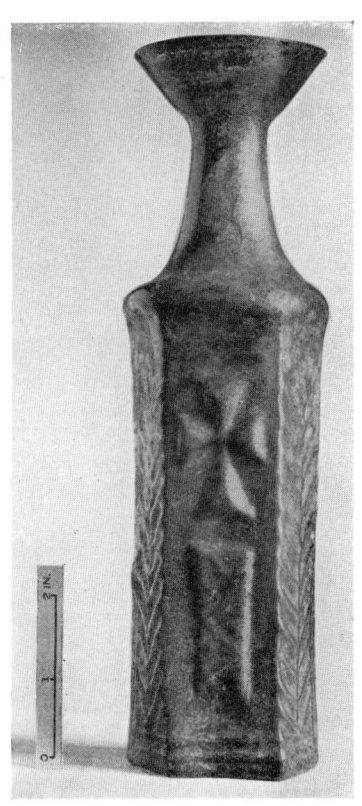

FIG. 92.—Bottle of blown glass, with cross: fifth century.

Moulded glass is represented by a bottle with a cross upon the front (Wall-Case 5 and fig. 92); and by small money-weights and pendants for necklaces (fig. 93) (fourth to sixth century) in Table-Case A, the former having names and busts of officials, the latter sacred subjects like the Good Shepherd.

144   INTRODUCTION

Coloured glass is best illustrated by the blue vases (fig. 64) of the late fifth or early sixth century from Amiens (*Samarobriva*), which may have been chalices (p. 106). It may be noted that a third-century vessel without handles, of dark-blue glass, obtained in Cairo and now in the Berlin Museum, is also ornamented with enamel-painting; it has upon it genii at the vintage and is conjectured to have been a chalice.

The glass of the Byzantine Empire is little known. Plain beakers and jugs have been found in Sicilian cemeteries with coins of the Emperor Maurice Tiberius (A. D. 582-602). Later times are scantily represented; the Treasury of St. Mark's,

Fig. 93.—Byzantine glass medallion with bust of Our Lord: eleventh century. (No. 686.)

Fig. 94.—Byzantine glass medallion with figure of St. Theodore: c. twelfth century. (No. 693.)

Fig. 95.—Glass pendant with the Good Shepherd: fourth century. (No. 697.)

Venice, however, contains chalices, patens, lamps, and other vessels, some of plain glass, some ornamented with conical or disk-shaped projections. The most remarkable object claimed as Byzantine is a cup with gilded and enamelled ornament and mythological subjects dating from the ninth or tenth century. This cup is interesting for comparison both with the much older example at Berlin mentioned above, and with early 'Saracenic' enamelled glass, of about its own date, illustrated by examples in the King Edward VII Gallery. 'Cameos' were moulded in coloured glass (figs. 94, 95).

Enamel. Byzantine enamel is almost exclusively of the 'cell' or cloisonné variety, in which the enamel is contained in cells or compartments formed by strips of gold set on edge and soldered in position. The metal employed is usually gold, more rarely silver or copper.

Jewellery with coloured stones fixed in cells in a similar way, but without aid of fire, was known in Egypt under the ancient dynasties, and in Assyria, in the steppe regions north of Persia, and very probably in Persia itself, many centuries before our era. But the earliest examples of enamels in cells of the same kind were discovered in Egypt with objects dating from the time of the Roman Empire. It is clear that, once acquired, the fashion rapidly spread, and must have been widely known in the sixth century. The most remarkable example dating from about that time is a cross-reliquary, probably made in Syria-Palestine or in Egypt, preserved for many centuries in the chapel called Sancta Sanctorum in the Lateran (cf. p. 44), and now in the Vatican Library. This cross is enamelled with whole Gospel subjects, the iconography of which points to Syria and shows that the enamellers of the period did not shrink from the most ambitious tasks. It may be assumed that circular enamels with busts, a type very frequent in later centuries, were already in existence at this time, since a gold brooch in the Museum (Iron Age Gallery, Wall-Case 61), dating from about A.D. 600, contains an enamelled bust, apparently an Ostrogothic imitation of an earlier eastern model. Between the sixth and the eleventh centuries cloisonné enamels on gold were made in Italy and the West, of which there are examples at Milan and elsewhere. Though enamels must have been made in numbers as early as the sixth century, examples are rare, among the best-known being the reliquary cross sent by the Emperor Justin to St. Radegund, still preserved at Poitiers.

The great period of Byzantine enamelling lies between the tenth and twelfth centuries, when the majority of the examples now in museums, churches, and monasteries were made, for the most part in Constantinople itself and in Georgia, which was then connected with the Empire and evidently became an important centre of production. Cloisonné enamels were probably produced in Persia, but some examples with Persian designs, such as plaques on the Pala d'Oro, or altar-piece, in St. Mark's at Venice, would seem to be the work of Byzantine craftsmen; the well-known ewer in the treasure of St. Maurice d'Agaune in the Valais has the best claim to a Persian origin. A copper bowl at Innsbruck, made in Mesopotamia in the time of a Turkish (Seljūk) prince in the twelfth century, is enamelled with 'Saracenic' subjects. The art of enamelling passed from Byzantine sources into Sicily, and small enamelled plaques are sewn to the ceremonial garments of the Sicilian kings, now preserved in Vienna. It is generally believed that the Chinese borrowed the art from the same source in the fourteenth century.

The metal employed being chiefly gold, the great majority of enamels are on small plaques which can be combined, if desired,

Fig. 96.—Byzantine gold ring: fourteenth century. (No. 171.)

Fig. 97.—Byzantine bronze ring with inscription: *c.* eleventh century. (No. 139.)

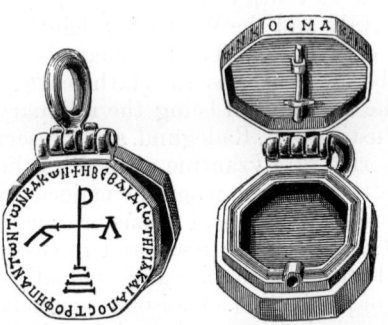

Fig. 98.—Byzantine gold and nielloed reliquary: 10th-11th century. (No. 284.)

for the ornamentation of large objects, such as the altar-pieces, book-covers, chalices, patens, reliquaries, frames of ikons or royal crowns, like that at Budapest mentioned above (p. 131). As a rule, the figure is fully enamelled, and the ground is provided by the gold plaque forming the base. The method adopted is to beat out of the thin gold plate a cavity giving the contour

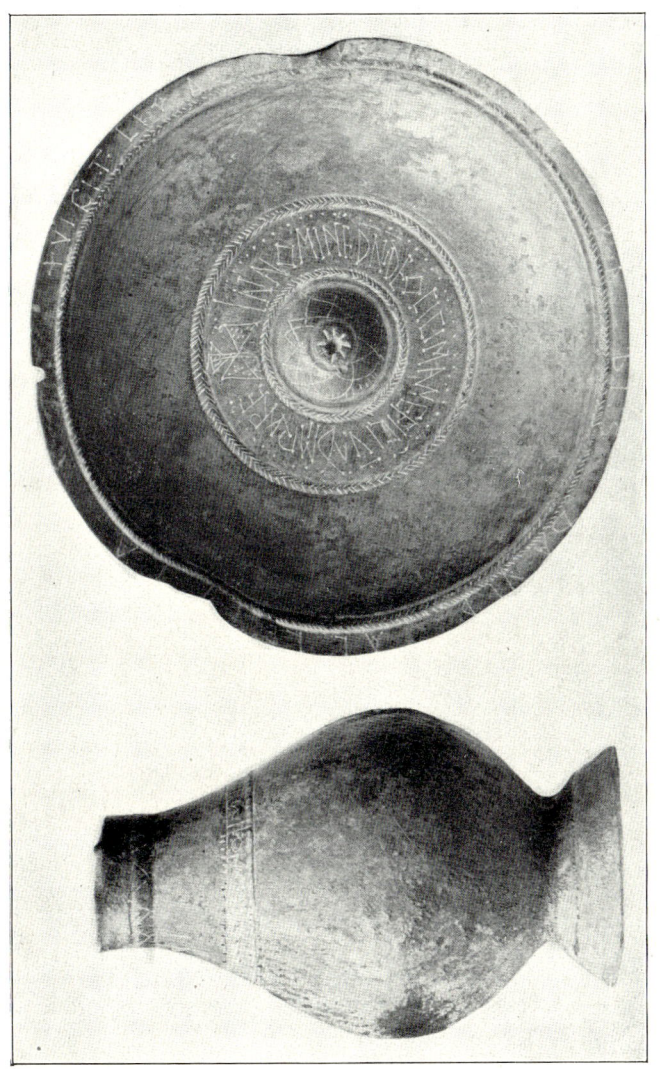

PLATE XII. BRONZE EWER AND BASIN FROM SPAIN.
(See p. 172.)

of the figure; the interior details, such as features, folds of garments, etc., are then filled in by means of soldered gold strips, and the enamel placed in the compartments thus formed. Often, however, the whole plate, ground and all, is covered with enamel. When this is the case, a vertical strip round the outer edge contains the enamel used for the ground, and the whole of each figure in the design is outlined by means of the soldered gold strips; the two medallions with busts of saints in Table-Case B are made by the latter method.

The subjects are in the great majority of cases religious; busts or figures of Our Lord, the Virgin, and saints, more rarely whole scenes such as the Crucifixion. Occasionally the design consists entirely of formal ornament such as floral scroll; this is the case with the early example at Poitiers (pp. 131, 145). Fine later examples are plaques from an ikon of the eleventh or twelfth century now in the Metropolitan Museum at New York.

Pottery for the most part consists of the red and buff unglazed wares with moulded, incised, or painted ornament, illustrated by the lamps, flasks, and domestic utensils (chiefly broken), which are so numerous in all large collections. Glazed ware is represented as early as the first century in Egypt; but Christian wares as a class do not appear to have rivalled the productions of the Mohammedan potters, though the discovery, near Preslav in Bulgaria, of glazed tiles, ascribed to the tenth century, with figure subjects and ornament suggesting Mesopotamian inspiration, shows how slight our knowledge is. Hitherto the only mediaeval glazed pottery described as Byzantine had consisted of fragmentary bowls, with designs of animals or monsters supposed to date from the period between the twelfth and fifteenth centuries.

Textiles. The most interesting form of textile, other than the figured silk described below, is the tapestry work from Egypt, preserved through burial with the dead in the dry Egyptian soil, and brought to light by the excavation of Coptic cemeteries. This tapestry, which was sometimes used upon hangings and curtains, served more often to adorn linen garments with coloured strips, bands, or medallions enriched with formal ornamental designs or human and animal figures. The designs were generally executed in dyed wool, though silk occasionally formed the weft.

During the first three centuries the subjects were Graeco-Roman in character, chiefly genii and mythological figures rendered with Hellenistic naturalism. The colours used were few; but in the fourth century a fuller scale was adopted, crimson, green, and yellow being now conspicuous, while Christian subjects took the place of pagan. The effect of some of the medallions with their elaborate compositions at first strikes the eye as grotesque; the persons in a scene or group are hard to distinguish, and there is no pretence of truth to

FIG. 99.—Tapestry medallion on a tunic from a Coptic cemetery. (No 951.)

nature. But in the first place the colour is admirable, and secondly these compositions do not aim at the correct reproduction of natural forms, but at the satisfaction of aesthetic feeling for rich pattern and colour. The effect of these designs with their fine dyes upon a natural flax background seldom fails to please: the medallion upon the grave-tunic in Wall-Case 25, apparently representing the Adoration of the Magi (fig. 99), gives an idea of the nature of this work. At some time before the fifth century the tapestry weavers learned the use of the draw-loom, and produced a weave resembling the twill of Byzantine silk fabrics, which allowed indefinite repetition of the pattern. It is believed that the makers of the figured silks made at Alexandria in the fifth and sixth centuries must have derived their weave from this, and transmitted it to Sassanian Persia.

Coptic tapestries are poorly represented in the Christian Room, the above-mentioned grave-tunic affording the best example, but there is a variety in the Department of Egyptian and Assyrian Antiquities (Fifth Egyptian Room, Table-Cases G and H); while the series in the Victoria and Albert Museum at South Kensington is one of the best in existence. It will be found instructive to compare Coptic tapestries with those made in Ancient Peru by similar methods, and exhibited among the collections from Ancient America: these Peruvian stuffs, with their rich colours and schematized designs, have many affinities to those of the Copts. The collection contains no example of the other linen stuffs with sacred subjects made in Egypt in these early centuries, and represented by fine examples at South Kensington. Here the method was to 'reserve' the design by covering it with wax before the whole fabric was dyed with purple or red; after the dyeing, the stuff was dried, and the removal of the wax left the subject in natural flax-colour on a purple ground. The same kind of method is still employed by the natives of Sumatra, and examples may be seen in the Asiatic section of the Ethnographical Gallery.

The figured silks of Christian times seem to have been first made in Alexandria, perhaps in the fourth century. The silk was apparently brought from Khotan in Chinese Turkestan; but though recent explorations in that part of the world have shown that the Chinese were producing figured silks during the Han period (B.C. 206–A.D. 220), there is no more trace of Chinese influence, either technical or artistic, in the early Alexandrian work than of Alexandrian influence on the Chinese. About the sixth century the Sassanian Persians, through whose territory much of the imported silk from China entered the West, were making silk with the Alexandrian twill mentioned above, a fact which suggests the inference that Persia may have learned silk-weaving from Egypt. Persian motives now became common, such as confronted beasts flanking the 'sacred tree', or pairs of mounted huntsmen; and these designs began to influence Chinese weavers, who by the seventh century reproduced Persian motives, but treated them in a Chinese manner.

Down to the sixth century the weavers in the East-Roman Empire had depended upon imported silk alone, and the silkworm was still unknown to them. But after the Emperor Justinian had succeeded in introducing the worm, sericulture spread with great rapidity, especially in Syria and in Greece. An imperial manufactory was established in Constantinople, while Thebes and Corinth were also centres of production. When the Arabs conquered Egypt and Syria, silks were still produced in those countries, but the motives now conformed to the taste of Islam. The basis of the ornament was chiefly Persian, but the scale was smaller, and Cufic inscriptions often served as decorative motives.

Textiles ornamented with figures and other designs were used for altar-coverings, as hangings and canopies and for other purposes, but their most general use was for garments, which were not only decorated with simple features, such as bands or borders, but with medallions or broad strips bearing figure subjects like those of Coptic tapestries; Asterius, bishop of Amasea in Asia Minor in the fourth century, rebukes the wealthy for wearing such garments, describing persons thus arrayed as 'walking frescoes'. In the mosaic scene in the church of St. Vitale at Ravenna representing Theodora with her suite we see on the broad lower border of the Empress's mantle the subject of the Adoration of the Magi. A high proportion of the figured fabrics now preserved formed part of costume, and, for the earlier centuries, that of lay persons rather than ecclesiastics.

Byzantine figured silks were famous down to the thirteenth century, but after that time the industry seems to have decayed. It had, however, been transplanted into Sicily by the Norman king Roger, in the middle of the twelfth century, and thence spread north into Italy. The earliest designs ornamenting figured silks are mythological and religious subjects in the Hellenistic style of Alexandria; of the latter class a fine example is the Annunciation, discovered in recent years in the above-mentioned Lateran Chapel (p. 145), and now in the Vatican Library. Later came the formal, almost heraldic beasts and birds of Persian descent, eagles, gryphons, lions or other creatures, alone or confronted, within circles interlacing with each other. Such fabrics are frequently mentioned in the *Liber Pontificalis* and in early inventories; the description of birds and beasts enclosed in 'wheels' (*rotae* or *rotellae*) indicates enclosure in the circles. Of great interest are textiles inscribed with names of emperors, such as the piece with lions and the names of the Emperors Romanus and Christophorus at Siegburg, dated between A.D. 920 and 931, and another piece with lions, now at Düsseldorf, with the names of Constan-

Fig. 100.—Silk textile with mounted figures from Egypt: sixth century.

tine VIII and Basil II, and therefore made between A.D. 976 and A.D. 1025.

Ancient figured silks have most commonly been preserved through having been buried in the coffins of princes or bishops, or used to enclose relics. Pieces with a design of elephants and the name of Peter, superintendent of the imperial manufactory at Constantinople, were found in the tomb of Charles the Great at Aix-la-Chapelle, though they probably date from the tenth or eleventh century; some remarkable pieces, found in the tomb of St. Cuthbert, are now in the Library of Durham Cathedral; while many examples are preserved in continental churches.

When through the general impoverishment of the last Byzantine period figured silk ceased to be manufactured, its place was taken by embroidery, a kind of work which had been used to enrich a plain ground with formal ornament or figure-subjects from the Early Christian centuries, but during the time when fine woven silks were made was perhaps regarded as of secondary importance. Many of the finest examples which remain are the *epitaphioi* or coverings for the ceremonial bier used in the Orthodox Greek Church on Good Friday. They are embroidered with figures of Our Lord in the tomb, and chiefly date from the latter part of the thirteenth century or even later. The well-known embroidered dalmatic in the Treasury of St. Peter's at Rome, traditionally associated with the name of Charles the Great, is now genera ascribed to the fourteenth century.

APPENDIX

I. COPTS AND ABYSSINIANS.

THE Egyptian Christians are called Copts from *Kubt*, the Arabic version of the Coptic form of the Greek word Αἰγύπτιος (Egyptian); they originally belonged to the ancient Egyptian stock, and in their general personal appearance still resemble their forefathers as known to us by the representations upon the monuments, though their features have been modified by intermarriage with Arabs and tribes of the Eastern Sudan. Coptic Christianity was derived from Alexandria, and the Scriptures were translated from the Greek perhaps by the middle of the third century (p. 6). In the fifth century Egypt was distracted by the Monophysite heresy (p. 159), which was condemned by the Council of Chalcedon in the year 451; but the Copts refusing to accept the condemnation, the schism became permanent, also affecting the Abyssinian Church, which descends directly from that of Egypt and shares the Monophysite belief. The Coptic Church was not exterminated by the Mahommedan Conquest in the seventh

Fig. 101.—Coptic tombstone: seventh-eighth century. (No. 942.)

century; indeed its relations with the conquerors were at first friendly, for the Copts had been so hardly used by their fellow Christians on account of their heretical beliefs that the Arab invasion was actually welcomed. But in the eighth and ninth centuries the Arabs began both to persecute and make proselytes, so that large numbers of Christians abandoned their faith and became Mahommedans; throughout the Middle Ages the condition of those Copts who did not embrace Islam was almost uniformly miserable. Nevertheless the Copts have preserved a sacred art in which East Christian tradition has been maintained, and during the Middle Ages the visits of Christian artists from other countries, especially Armenia, doubtless renewed the sources of their inspiration. The subjects carved upon the wooden doors from the Church of Al-Mu 'Allaka at Cairo (Wall-Cases 5 and 6, plate XIII) prove that there was no rupture in tradition; at the same time the panels filled with decorative designs illustrate a strong Saracenic influence in the field of ornament.

Abyssinia, a mountainous country in which the Blue Nile takes its rise, lies to the south of Egypt and Nubia, and is inhabited by a mixed population of Hamitic, Semitic, and Negro blood. It owed much of its early civilization to Arabs from Yemen, who entered the country before the Christian era, and were for a long time accessible to Graeco-Roman influence; its capital was Axum. Christianity had been formally introduced from Egypt by the fourth century (p. 6); Frumentius, the first bishop, was consecrated by Athanasius, A.D. 340—346. The Abyssinians joined with the Copts in adopting the Monophysite belief: the *Abuna*, or head of the Abyssinian Church, is still a Copt nominated by the Patriarch of Alexandria. From the fifth century to the end of the Middle Ages little was heard of this Ethiopian kingdom; but in the early sixteenth century the Portuguese made it known to Europe, and their missionaries endeavoured to convert its inhabitants to Latin Christianity. Their efforts were, however, unsuccessful, and in the first half of the seventeenth century the missionaries were expelled from the country, which was once more to a great extent cut off from European influences. At the close of the seventeenth century a new era of exploration was inaugurated by the voyage of the French doctor Poncet, who was followed in the eighteenth century by the British traveller James Bruce.

As might be expected from the savage environment of the country and the long periods during which it remained in

PLATE XIII. CEDAR PANELS FROM CAIRO: THE ANNUNCIATION, BAPTISM AND ASCENSION. (No. 986.)

(See pp. 171, 172.)

isolation, the Christian belief in Abyssinia has been much corrupted by superstitious beliefs and practices, while various ideas and usages have also been adopted from Jewish and Mahommedan sources.

The clergy and the monks, who are very numerous, are almost the only persons in the country with any pretensions to learning, and their knowledge is chiefly confined to a superficial acquaintance with a book of the Gospels, the Psalms,

FIG. 102.—Abyssinian priest holding crutch at entrance to the Holy of Holies (after J. T. Bent, *The Sacred City of the Ethiopians*).

the liturgies, and the lives of saints. The Abyssinian Church has retained the Christian sacraments and feasts, and the fasts which are prescribed, but not universally observed, occupy more than a third of the year. The Abyssinian liturgy belongs to the same family as that of the Copts, and, like it, is a descendant of the Alexandrian liturgy of St. Mark. Allusion has already been made to the circular thatched churches, with their resemblance in type to the native hut (fig. 59), to the wooden altar slabs upon which the chalices are placed (p. 114), and to the ornate processional-crosses (p. 114, plate XV). We may here further notice the brass- or ivory-headed crutch (fig. 102), and the rattle, curiously resembling the ancient Egyptian sistrum, both used by priests in religious dances (fig. 104); the crutch also serves as a support during the long services, for there are no church seats. A cross, sometimes with ostrich eggs fixed on the points, surmounts every church, and hangs in the Holy of Holies; in this connexion it may be of interest to mention that all over Western Asia, as well as in Egypt and Abyssinia, ostrich eggs may often be seen hanging in churches and

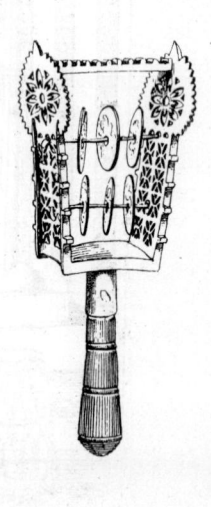

Fig. 103.—Abyssinian silver chalice.

Fig. 104.—Abyssinian priest's rattle.

mosques, where they are probably placed as symbols of the creation, recalling a very ancient belief that the world was produced from an egg. Though here and there European bells have been introduced, the ordinary church-bells of Ethiopia are large slabs of wood or slate-like stone suspended from a bar, and similar to the wooden *simantra* (see p. 97) commonly used in the Greek Church. The common symbol of Christianity is a blue string worn round the neck. The liturgical language of Abyssinia is Ethiopic or *Ge'ez*, a

Semitic tongue akin to that used in early times by the Arabs of Yemen (see above); the name, which is in full *Lisana Ge'ez*, means 'the tongue of the free', and the syllabary is written from right to left. Owing to conquests by Gallas and people from Tigré, a number of foreign words were gradually introduced, and new signs were invented to express them; eventually the dialect of the province of Amhara became predominant, with the result that Amharic is now the general language of the country. The manuscript exhibited in Wall-Case 27 is written in *Ge'ez*, and the inscriptions on the metal crosses are also examples of that character.

II. THE GREEK CHURCH.

The Orthodox Eastern Church is practically a federation of autonomous National Churches in communion with one another, agreeing exactly in doctrine and almost exactly in rites, customs, and discipline; but, unlike the Latin Church, acknowledging no central authority. In the case of a general synod, however, the Patriarch of Constantinople would probably preside.

These National Churches are:—

1. The Patriarchate of Constantinople, consisting of Turkey in Europe, most of Asia Minor, and Cyprus.
2. The Patriarchate of Alexandria, comprising Egypt.
3. The Patriarchate of Antioch, including all Syria except Palestine, and having an undefined eastern boundary.
4. The Patriarchate of Jerusalem, confined to Palestine.
5. The Church of Russia, by far the largest and most important of these Churches.
6. The Church of Greece.
7. The Church of Serbia.
8. The Church of Roumania.
9. The Church of Montenegro.
10. The Church of Bosnia and Herzegovina.
11. The Orthodox Eastern Church in Austria-Hungary.

The four Patriarchates are governed by Patriarchs, and the other Churches by their respective 'Holy Governing Synods' or by some chief metropolitan. Their relations to one another and to the See of Constantinople are not unlike those of the Episcopal Churches of England, Scotland, Ireland, the British Colonies, and the United States to one another and to the See of Canterbury.

Notwithstanding considerable divergence in rites, customs,

and discipline, the Latin Church of the West and the Greek Church of the East continued in communion with one another until the year 1054, when a series of disputes extending over some centuries culminated in a definite schism, which, in spite of several attempts at reunion, has continued to this day. The chief doctrinal points of difference are:—

1. The question of the universal jurisdiction of the Roman Pontiff.

2. The insertion by the Latins of the words 'and the Son' (*Filioque*) in the clause of the Constantinopolitan Creed defining the Procession of the Holy Spirit.

3. The doctrines of the intermediate state of the Departed, more exactly defined by the Latins than by the Greeks.

4. A question as to whether the consecration is effected in the Eucharist, as the Latins hold, by the Words of Institution, or, according to the Greeks, by the *Epiklesis* or Invocation of the Holy Spirit.

On almost all other points, allowing for a greater tendency to exact definition in the Latin Church, the doctrines of the two Churches are hardly distinguishable, though the Eastern Church does not recognize as authoritative the definitions of any of the Councils, called by the Latins Œcumenical, which were subsequent to the seventh General Council in A.D. 787.

The chief differences of outward observance are:—

1. The marriage of the Eastern parochial clergy, celibacy being only exacted from monks, and from bishops, who are always chosen from monasteries.

2. The administration of the Holy Communion to the laity in both kinds by the Easterns.

3. The use of leavened bread for the Eucharist, the Latins using unleavened.

4. The prohibition by the Greeks of the use of images, as distinguished from pictures, for purposes of devotion.

5. The use by the Eastern Church of Baptism by immersion only, Baptism by affusion, the common practice of the Western Church, being regarded as of doubtful validity.

6. The prohibition by the Eastern Church of the use of musical instruments in divine service.

7. The use in the East of vernacular or quasi-vernacular languages in divine service.

Nevertheless, all these differences of practice are allowed to be retained by certain bodies of Christians of the Oriental Rite, known as 'Uniats', who have placed themselves under the jurisdiction of the See of St. Peter.

III. HERESIES, AND GNOSTICISM.

Of the various heresies which distracted the Church during the first three centuries many originated in the East, where some still count adherents. Most of them, however, soon died out, and, with the exception of the different sects of the doubtfully Christian Gnostics, left little or no archaeological evidence of their existence. It was not until the Œcumenical Councils of the fourth century began to legislate for the Church at large that important separated religious bodies, consisting of those who refused to accept the creeds and definitions of those councils, were formed.

The principal of these bodies were:—

1. The *Arians*, who denied that the Son is consubstantial with the Father. These were condemned by the First General Council of Nicaea in A.D. 325. Though this heresy at one time seemed likely to prevail, and though it attracted to itself most of the newly formed Teutonic nations, it eventually died out, leaving very few traces behind it.

2. The *Nestorians* (p. 5), who, affirming that the Divinity and Humanity of Christ are not only two Natures (φύσεις), but also two Persons (ὑποστάσεις), refused the title of Theotokos (Mother of God) to the Virgin Mary. These were condemned by the Third General Council at Ephesus in the year 431. Their tenets were adopted by the East Syrian and Persian part of the Church; but after a long and successful missionary career in Central Asia, China, and India, they were overwhelmed by the conquests of Timur in the fourteenth century, and are now only represented by a small community in the neighbourhood of Urumiah, where Persia and Turkey in Asia meet, and also by the Chaldaean and Malabar Uniats, who have finally abjured their heresy and joined themselves to Rome.

3. The *Eutychians* or *Monophysites*, who hold the exact opposite to Nestorianism, affirming that the Divinity and Humanity of Christ are not two Natures but one. These were condemned by the Council of Chalcedon in A.D. 451. A great part of the West Syrian Church, the Copts of Egypt, the Abyssinians, and to some extent the Armenians, adopted this heresy in its various forms; and so at a later period, after the Portuguese conquests, did the so-called Christians of St. Thomas in India, who were originally Nestorians. From an important leader, Jacobus Baradaeus, the Monophysites

were called *Jacobites*, and at the same period the name *Melchites* or Royalists was applied to the Orthodox Syrians as adherents of the party of the Emperor of the East. The rites of the West Syrians, Copts, Abyssinians and Armenians, corrected in a Catholic direction, are also used by communities in Syria, Egypt, Abyssinia, Armenia, and in various other countries who have united themselves to Rome.

4. The *Monothelites*, who held the orthodox doctrine as to the one Person and two Natures of Christ, but affirmed that the Divinity and Humanity had but one Will, the Divine. They were supported by the Emperor Heraclius, but were finally condemned by the Sixth General Council, the third of Constantinople, in A.D. 680. Most of the Monothelites were eventually absorbed by the Monophysites, but one community, the Maronites of the Lebanon, continued to exist as a separate body until a little before the year 1200 they were united with the Roman Church, though to this day they retain their own rites and customs.

This recrudescence of the decaying Roman mythology had less influence on the course of contemporary Christian thought than the intrusion of the various Gnostic beliefs a couple of centuries earlier; a few words must therefore be said on the subject of Gnosticism, though the Museum Collection of Gnostic Gems and Amulets is in Table-Case I of the Egyptian Room in the Department of Egyptian and Assyrian Antiquities. Gnostic, an adjective derived from the Greek substantive *gnosis* (knowledge), signified one who assumed a superior knowledge, by which the scheme of the universe and the destiny of man might be revealed. It has been said of the Gnostics that they considered the revelation as preached by the Church a bare minimum of truth, just sufficient for an ordinary intelligence, but too rudimentary for those who claimed to know the hidden mysteries of existence. They held that salvation was to be won not so much by faith or by works as by mystic knowledge (*gnosis*), and if their contention had prevailed, Christianity would have lost its moral force and become little more than a system of cosmogony. Gnosticism was older than Christianity, and was a product of the taste for abstract speculation, common alike to the Greek and Oriental genius. After the Asiatic campaigns of Alexander the Great, the Greek world became better acquainted with the principal religions of the East, and thoughtful men began to hope that by a union of Greek philosophy, especially Platonism, with the best elements of Oriental beliefs, the problem of man's place in the universe might be solved. The intellectual movements inaugurated by this hope were based on a sincere desire to widen and deepen the foundations of religion, and were already in full activity in Egypt and Syria when the advent of Christianity opened a new field to pagan seekers after truth. To the manifold elements of the Gnostic system originating in Egypt, Syria, Judaea, Mesopotamia, and Persia were now added others derived from the new faith, and in proportion as these assumed a predominant place, the Gnostics were assimilated to the Christian community. This approximation was at some times far closer than at others, for they were divided into various sects following the doctrines of different teachers; and while some of these lay beyond the pale of the Church, others incorporated into their scheme of the universe so many Christian beliefs that they actually formed sects within the Christian organization. It is impossible in this place to do more than indicate some of the more prominent theories of Gnosticism, but about the beginning of the Christian era most of them were ultimately based on a dualism similar in some respects to that of the ancient Persian religion. On the one hand there was a Supreme Being or infinite spiritual existence; on the other, matter, the source of all evil. From the Supreme Being issued a number of emanations called *aeons*, conceived as Divine qualities—Reason, Truth, Power, and the like—which together constituted a World of Light and Divine Fullness known as the *Pleroma*. One of these aeons fell under the influence of matter, and there thus arose a series of intermediate beings, and finally the human race, in which the higher and lower elements of spirit and matter are blended. All men are thus in need of redemption from the grosser element, and their hope of liberation is greater or less in proportion as the spiritual element predominates over the material. It is easy to see how the Christian doctrine of the redemption of the world would appeal to men holding a theory of this kind, and to imagine how those Gnostics who were most in sympathy with Christianity might bring their views into accord with Christian belief.

While the inner or esoteric doctrines of Gnosticism were due to deep philosophic and religious aspirations, it also had a more popular aspect which betrays the magical superstitions of earlier times. The personifications and ideas, which to the adept needed no visible form, were represented for the benefit of less subtle minds by symbolic figures of a fantastic description, and were accompanied by mystical words and formulae to which, especially when engraved on particular kinds of stone, a magical power was ascribed. To produce their full effect these words of power had to be pronounced by men ceremonially pure, dressed in a certain manner, and speaking in a certain tone of voice; while for the invocation of the greatest names particular ceremonies were necessary. Most of these names were formed out of the initial letters of a number of magical words, and have no intrinsic meaning. The most widely known is *Abraxas* or *Abrasax*, a manifestation of the Supreme Deity, who is constantly seen upon Gnostic gems and amulets. He is usually represented with a cock's head, emblematic of the sun, a human body, two serpents instead of legs, and with a shield and whip in his hands (fig. 105). In the field are frequently engraved the names Iao and Abraxas in Greek characters. The former word has been identified with the great name of the Hebrew God Jah, and is often accompanied on Gnostic gems by two other Hebrew words, *Adonai* and *Sabaoth* (Lord of Hosts), which also denote the Supreme Deity. The origin of the word Abraxas is obscure, but it is generally explained by the fact that the Greek letters of which it is composed are also numerals, which, added together, make 365—the number of heavens of which Abraxas was lord; the first part of it is perhaps related to another magical word, *Abracadabra*, which was very popular in the declining years of the Roman Empire and in the Middle Ages in Western Europe. Another popular Gnostic symbol was the serpent *Khnoubis*, derived from Egyptian mythology, and representing the creative principle personified by the Egyptians under the name of *Khnemu*; while among the names of magical power, those of angels were conspicuous, especially those of Michael, Gabriel, Uriel, Salathiel, and Raphael.

FIG. 105.—Abraxas, from a Gnostic gem.

Gnosticism, which chiefly flourished in Egypt, reached its height in the third century, and was sinking into insignificance in the fourth. It is represented by remains found in these islands. In 1827 a thin sheet of gold inscribed with Gnostic charms was discovered close to the Roman fort of Segontium near Carnarvon, and a Gnostic gem found at Silchester is in the Reading Museum; it is possible that the Abraxas gem in the ring of Bishop Seffrid (A.D. 1125-1151) in Chichester Cathedral was discovered in England.

IV. IMPORTANT DATES

First Century

A.D.
- 64. Persecution in the reign of Nero.
- 70. Taking of Jerusalem by Titus.

Second Century

- 112. Pliny the Younger, Legate of Bithynia, writes to Trajan as to the treatment of Christians in his province.
- 117. Hadrian builds the new city of Aelia Capitolina at Jerusalem.
- 161. Persecution in the reign of Marcus Aurelius.

Third Century

- 202. Abgar IX, Prince of Edessa, adopts Christianity as the State religion.
- 226. Beginning of the Sassanian dynasty in Persia.
- 249-50. Persecution in the reign of Decius.
- 299-300. Trdat (Tiridates) III, adopts Christianity as the State religion in Armenia.

Fourth Century

- 313. Accession of Constantine. Toleration of Christianity in the Roman Empire.
- 323. Constantine sole ruler. Christianity recognized as State religion.
- 324. Foundation of Constantinople.
- 325. First General Council at Nicaea. The Arian heresy condemned.
- 381. Second General Council at Constantinople.
- 395. Division of the Empire under Arcadius (East) and Honorius (West), sons of Theodosius.

Fifth Century

- 403. Honorius makes Ravenna his capital.
- 410. Sack of Rome by Alaric.
  The Roman legions abandon Britain.
- 429. The Vandals invade Africa.
- 431. Third General Council at Ephesus. Nestorius condemned; the title 'Mother of God' recognized.
- 437-8. St. Patrick begins the conversion of Ireland.
- 439. The Vandals complete the conquest of Africa by taking Carthage.
- 449-73. The Jutes establish themselves in Kent.
- 451. Defeat of Attila, King of the Huns, by Aëtius at Châlons.
  Fourth General Council at Chalcedon. The Monophysite heresy condemned.
- 455. Sack of Rome by Genseric, King of the Vandals. The vessels from the Temple of Jerusalem carried off.
- 476. Fall of the Roman Empire in the West by the deposition of Romulus Augustulus at Ravenna. The political centre of gravity henceforward once more at Rome.
- 481. Clovis founds the dynasty of the Merovingian Franks.
- 493. Theodoric the Ostrogoth takes Ravenna and founds a kingdom in Italy.
- 496. Clovis baptized by St. Remy.

Sixth Century

507. Clovis drives the Visigoths from all Gaul except the south-east.
526. Death of Theodoric.
527. Justinian Emperor in the East. (527-565).
533. Belisarius, general of Justinian, takes Carthage and recovers Africa from the Vandals.
535. Belisarius takes Sicily and begins the reconquest of Italy from the Goths.
546. Rome taken by Totila, King of the Goths: the city remains empty for forty days.
549. Justinian's armies invade Spain; the south-east coast remains Byzantine for sixty years (to A.D. 615).
552. Narses, general of Justinian, completes the reconquest of Italy.
    The silkworm brought into the Byzantine Empire, probably from Khotan in Chinese Turkestan.
553. Fifth General Council at Constantinople.
563. Columba founds his monastery on Iona.
578. The Lombards establish a kingdom in the north of Italy.
587. Recared I, first Catholic King of Spain.
597. Augustine, sent by Gregory the Great, lands at Ebbsfleet in Kent.

Seventh Century

614. The Persians take Jerusalem, and carry off the Holy Cross (recovered by Heraclius in A.D. 629).
634-40. Egypt and Syria-Palestine conquered by the Mohammedans.
651. Persia conquered by the Mohammedans: end of the native Sassanian dynasty founded in 226 B.C.
664. Synod of Whitby.
668. Theodore of Tarsus, in Cilicia, appointed Archbishop of Canterbury.
673-7. Mohammedans besiege Constantinople.
680. Sixth General Council at Constantinople.
692. Seventh General Council (*in Trullo*) at Constantinople.

Eighth Century

709. Mohammedans take N. Africa from the Byzantine Empire.
711. Mohammedans take Spain from the Visigoths.
717-18. Mohammedans again besiege Constantinople.
725-6. Beginning of Iconoclasm under the Emperor Leo III.
732. Charles Martel defeats the Mohammedans near Poitiers.
750. End of the Ummayad Caliphate at Damascus; the Abbāsid dynasty begins at Baghdad.
752. Ravenna taken from the Byzantine Empire by Aistulf, King of the Lombards; end of Byzantine rule in northern and central Italy.
    End of the Merovingian (earlier Frankish) Dynasty; Pepin, son of Charles Martel, proclaimed King of the Franks at Soissons.
754. Pepin is crowned by the Pope: he expels the Lombards from Italy.
756. Caliphate of Cordova established by the fugitive Ummayad, Abd. Er-Rahman.
771. Charles the Great sole King of the Franks.
774. Charles the Great ends the Lombard power.
781. At the request of Charles the Great, Alcuin of York directs education in the Frankish dominions.

IMPORTANT DATES 165

787. Second Council of Nicaea authorizes the veneration of images (pictures). First attack of the Northmen on England.
800. Charles the Great crowned Emperor of the West at Rome. Beginning of the 'Holy Roman Empire'.

Ninth Century

827. The Arabs begin the conquest of Sicily, not completed for fifty years.
842. End of Iconoclasm; restoration of images (pictures) in the East.
867. Accession of Basil I at Constantinople.
The Danes conquer Northumbria.
869. Eighth General Council, at Constantinople, the last recognized by the Western Church.
870. Danish conquest of East Anglia.
871. Accession of King Alfred.
878. Battle of Ethandun: Wessex, Sussex, and Kent remain English, the rest of England under the Danes.

Tenth Century

904. Salonika sacked by the Saracens.
917–23. Simeon, Tsar of the Bulgarians, defeats the Byzantine armies and threatens Constantinople.
961. Crete recovered from the Mohammedans by the Emperor Nicephorus Phocas.
962. Otto I, the Saxon, crowned Emperor.
973. Accession of Otto II, who in the previous year had married Theophano daughter of the Byzantine Emperor Romanus.
976. Basil II Emperor in the East (976–1025).
983. Otto III Emperor in the West.
c.990. Conversion of the Russians under Vladimir.

Eleventh Century

1009. The Holy Sepulchre destroyed by the Fatimite Caliph.
1014–18. Basil II finally defeats the Bulgarians.
1040–3. The Normans take Apulia.
1053. Final rupture of the Greek and Latin Churches.
1060–90. The Normans conquer Sicily from the Saracens.
1071. Battle of Manzikert (Malazgerd): defeat of the Byzantine army under the Emperor Romanus by the Seljūk Turks under Alp Arslan.
1076. The Seljūks take Jerusalem.
1099. First Crusade. Recapture of Jerusalem; beginning of the Latin Kingdom of Jerusalem.

Twelfth Century

1147. Second Crusade.
c.1160. The great period of Serbian history begins with the Nemanya dynasty.
1186. Fall of the Latin Kingdom of Jerusalem.
1188–92. Third Crusade against Saladin.

Thirteenth Century

1202-4. Fourth Crusade. Capture of Constantinople. Beginning of the Latin interregnum. Baldwin of Flanders the first Latin Emperor.
1261. Restoration of the Byzantine Empire under Michael VIII, Palaeologus.

Fourteenth Century

1326-38. The Ottoman Turks take Brusa, Nicaea, and Nicomedia.
1356. The Turks cross the Hellespont and take Adrianople (1361).
1389. The Serbs defeated by the Turks at Kossovo.

Fifteenth Century

1402. Timur defeats the Ottoman Sultan Bajazet at Angora, thus giving the Byzantine Empire a reprieve.
1430. The Ottoman Murad II takes Salonika.
1453. Capture of Constantinople by Mahomet II. Fall of the Byzantine Empire.

DESCRIPTION OF CASES

Wall-Cases 1 and 2.

THE upper part of the cases contains a number of bronze lamps and other bronze objects dating mostly from the fifth to the seventh century. Of the lamps, some are suspended, others fixed on pricket stands (see the fine example, No. 496, fig. 9). The openwork disks hanging by chains are lamp-holders (*polycandela*), with circular holes round the edge which probably contained glass lamps. Along the top of the slope are several bronze censers with religious subjects in relief, some with chains (sixth to seventh century).

On the slope itself are arranged more recent objects of devotional use made, for the most part, for members of the Greek Church, chiefly in Russia; enamelled brass ikons and crosses of the seventeenth and eighteenth centuries; small devotional carvings in wood and ivory, including one of the wooden crosses inscribed with minute designs attributed to Mount Athos; a lead medallion with the Death of the Virgin and other objects. A carved wooden panel signed by Michael Condopidius of Naxos, representing the illness of St. Francis, illustrates the work of a Greek under Italian influence.

In order to give a general idea of a Russian enamelled cross of the seventeenth or eighteenth century, a typical example has been reproduced (plate XIV). The following account of the various inscriptions upon it will doubtless be of use to those who may possess articles of a similar nature. In the upper part are represented the first and third persons of the Trinity; at the top is God the Father, described by the words *Lord God Sabaoth*, with both hands extended, the fingers raised in the act of benediction; beneath is the dove with the inscription *Holy Spirit* above it; on either side are two descending angels, with the legend *Angels of God* on two separate labels, beneath which are two other words *King of Glory* (*Tsar Slavui*).

Above the head of Our Lord are the four initial letters of the words *Jesus of Nazareth, King of the Jews*; and in the angles of the cross contained in the nimbus, the two Greek words ὁ ὤν, which signify 'The existing', i.e. the eternal (One). The long inscription above the arms of Our Lord reads, *The Crucifixion of Our Lord and Saviour Jesus Christ the Son of God*; and that below the arms: *We adore thy Cross, O Lord, and glorify thy holy resurrection*, which is a verse from the *Troparion* (or anthem) sung at the *Stavroproskynesis* or Adoration of the Cross on the third Sunday in Lent and also upon Holy Cross Day. Beyond the arms of the cross are the first and last letters (IC XC) of the two Greek words 'Ιησοῦς Χριστός, Jesus Christ. Below, on either side of Our Lord's body and divided in two halves by it is the word *Nika*, victory; the letters K (*Kopie*) and T (*Trost*), meaning lance and reed respectively, which are almost always placed by the side of these instruments of the Passion, are here by exception absent. On the foot of the cross are two pairs of letters, the uppermost M and L signifying *Miesto lobnoe* or *place of a skull*, the lower pair P (R) and B, *Raspiat byst*, He was crucified. On the conventional hill from which the cross rises are two further pairs of letters, the first Γ (G), A, standing for *Glava Adama*, 'the skull of Adam', the second Γ (G), Γ (G), for *Gora Golgotha*, 'the Mount of Golgotha'. In the centre of the mount is seen the skull of Adam, in allusion to the tradition, commonly reproduced in Byzantine art, that the first man was buried upon the site where Christ was crucified. On the back of the upper part of the cross is another inscription, very commonly placed in this position, reading as follows: *The Cross, the guardian of the whole Universe; the Cross, the beauty of the Church; the Cross, to kings dominion; the Cross, to believers safety; the Cross, to angels glory; the Cross, to devils wounding;* the whole being taken from the *Exaposteilarion*, a sort of anthem used at Orthros or morning service on Wednesdays and Fridays.

It will be noticed that, as universally in Byzantine and Greek representations of the Crucifixion, and also in Western representations earlier than the thirteenth century, Our Lord's feet are nailed separately and not crossed one above the other. The cross with eight extremities, as shown in the plate, is that especially associated with the *Raskolniks* or dissenters of the Russian Church. But it is also in general use among the Orthodox.

At the bottom of the case are miscellaneous objects; fragments of linen tunics from Coptic cemeteries, one with a cross in purple, the other with H, and a heavy iron penitential crown from the Monastery of Kieff, of a type formerly worn by Russian ascetics and represented by examples in the National Historical Museum at Moscow. The large oval pebble with cross and Syriac inscription served as a tombstone for a Nestorian Christian of the thirteenth or fourteenth century in the province of Semirechensk, N. of Lake Issik Kul (fig. 2). At the back is a board with an edict against Christians promulgated in Japan in 1682.

PLATE XIV. RUSSIAN ENAMELLED BRASS CROSS.
(*See* p. 167.)

Wall-Cases 3 and 4.

Upper Shelves. Casts of some important Early Christian and Byzantine ivory-carvings in various collections.

a. Ivories in the British Museum[1] (originals in the King Edward VII Gallery, Bay xx, Table-Case and Pier-Case). The earliest are two well-known sets of plaques from caskets of about the beginning of the fifth century; one (No. 292, *8*) containing three panels with two fragments carved with conventional scrolls, the other (No. 291, *7*, plate II) four panels. The first set shows Moses striking the rock, St. Peter raising Tabitha from the dead, St. Paul conversing with Thecla, and the stoning of St. Paul. The subjects of the second set are: (1) Pilate washing his hands, Our Lord bearing the Cross, and the Denial of St. Peter; (2) the Death of Judas, and the Crucifixion; (3) the Maries at the Sepulchre; and (4) the Incredulity of St. Thomas. The Crucifixion scene is among the earliest known (p. 88). The style of all these casket-panels recalls contemporary sarcophagi. No. 294, *10*, plate III, is an early example of the Baptism, perhaps North Italian work of the sixth century. Conspicuous among the ivories from the Christian East is the magnificent leaf of a diptych (No. 295, *11*) with a figure of the Archangel Michael (frontispiece, plate I). It belongs to an early period, perhaps going back as far as the reign of Theodosius (A. D. 375–95), though considered by some to date from the time of Justinian. At the top is a Greek inscription: *Receive these gifts, and having learned the cause*—, doubtless continued upon a second leaf, now lost; this may have borne the figure of an emperor to whom the angel offered the orb as an emblem of sovereignty. Written in ink on the sunk surface at the back, originally intended for the wax, is a prayer in a hand of the seventh century, of which only a small proportion is legible. No. 302a, *20* (plate V) is a remarkable panel from a Byzantine casket (tenth to twelfth century), representing two scenes from the history of Joseph. On the left, the patriarch Jacob blesses Ephraim and Manasseh; on the right is the death of Jacob. Worthy of special remark are the 'pyxides' (cylindrical boxes). No. 297, *12* (plate IV) has the Martyrdom of St. Menas of Alexandria, in which city it was probably made in the course of the sixth century. On one side the saint is seen before the Roman judge; on the other, he stands, clothed in the long chlamys marking his rank, at the entrance to his sanctuary between the two camels (p. 180). No. 298, *13* (plate IV) shows Daniel in the usual oriental costume standing in the attitude of

---

[1] Where two catalogue-numbers are quoted, the first refers to the *Catalogue of Early Christian Antiquities*, the second, in italics, to the *Catalogue of Ivory Carvings*.

prayer (cf. p. 81) between lions, while Habakkuk guided by an angel brings him food: on the other side is a symbolical scene. No. 289, *3*, is an earlier pagan example, probably of the fourth century: boxes of this kind are known to have been used as reliquaries in Christian churches. No. 43 in the *Catalogue of Ivory Carvings* is a Carolingian copy of an East Christian model, carved with the Healing of the Demoniac. *Other ivories in the collection not represented by casts in this Case* are: a fine central panel from a book-cover of the sixth century probably carved in Syria, with the Adoration of the Magi and the Nativity, and on the back, written in ink, a prayer in a hand of the twelfth century; a small square plaque from a Byzantine casket (No. 302, *22*), representing the Archangel Michael in the scene of the Expulsion from Eden (tenth to twelfth century); a large Byzantine triptych showing the Crucifixion with Saints, and a panel with the *Deësis* (Our Lord between the Virgin and St. John the Baptist), both of the eleventh century; a diptych with busts of Apostles, Saints and Angels (twelfth century), and a side leaf of a triptych of similar date with a bust of St. John the Baptist and a figure of a bishop making the gesture of benediction; a panel (No. 296, *27*) with the Raising of Lazarus, either made in Egypt in the sixth century, as part of a series ornamenting an episcopal chair, or else an Italo-Byzantine work of the twelfth century made in the south of Italy; two Byzantine panels (ninth to tenth century) with the Vision of Ezekiel (No. 299, *18*), and the Nativity and Washing of the Infant Jesus (No. 300, *19*); two Byzantine panels from a casket with acrobats in the Hippodrome of Constantinople (No. 301, *16*, ninth century); a small panel from a casket with male figures (*Catalogue of Ivory Carvings*, No. *173*, Byzantine, ninth and tenth century); No. 302b, *23*, a panel with the Entry into Jerusalem. For the Melisenda book-cover see p. 188.

b. Reproductions of ivories of which the originals are not in the British Museum. Consular and private diptychs: the consul Stilicho (about A. D. 400) with his wife Serena and their son Eucherius, in the Treasury of the Cathedral of Monza; Flavius Taurus Clementinus (A. D. 513), consul at Constantinople, in the Liverpool Museum; Anastasius, consul at Constantinople (A. D. 517), in the Royal Museum, Berlin; Magnus (?), consul at Constantinople (A. D. 518), in the Bibliothèque Nationale, Paris; Justinianus, consul at Constantinople (A. D. 521), Trivulzio Collection, Milan; Philoxenus, consul at Constantinople (A.D. 525), Bibliothèque Nationale, Paris; an anonymous consular diptych of the fifth or sixth century in the Treasury of the Cathedral at Halberstadt. Mythological subjects appear on the leaf of a diptych of the third century at Sens representing Diana Lucifera (bearer of light), standing, with a torch, in a car drawn by two bulls, and below her is the Personification of the Sea, with marine animals. Aesculapius the physician, with Telesphorus the spirit of healing, and Hygieia (Health) (fourth century), in the Liverpool Museum; a muse and a bald-headed male figure, possibly a poet, (sixth century), in the Treasury of the Cathedral of Monza. The following have religious subjects: a diptych at Monza with David on one leaf and St. Gregory the Great (Pope, A. D. 590–604) on the other, by some regarded as a consular diptych converted to a religious use; diptych with Adam in the Garden of Eden and scenes from the life of St. Paul, in the Bargello at Florence (fifth to sixth century); another with Our Lord, and the Virgin and Child (sixth century), in the Kaiser Friedrich Museum, Berlin; book-cover composed of five panels (sixth century) in the Bibliothèque Nationale, Paris, having as the central subjects Our Lord between SS. Peter and Paul, and the Virgin between two angels; the leaf of a Byzantine diptych showing the Crucifixion (thirteenth century), in the Louvre, Paris; panel representing Our Lord crowning the Emperor Romanus IV (A. D. 1068–71) and his consort Eudocia, in the Bibliothèque Nationale, Paris.

Two panels are of Carolingian (Frankish) origin. The original of the first forms the ornament of a book-cover in the Bodleian Library at Oxford, the central compartment having Our Lord trampling on the lion and dragon, and the surrounding compartments Biblical scenes (eighth to ninth century). The other reproduces one leaf of a diptych of similar origin and date in the Louvre, with David dictating his psalms, the companion leaf (not exhibited) representing the Judgement of Solomon. On the top shelf, with the above-mentioned casts of pyxides in the Museum collection, is a reproduction of the large fourth-century example at Berlin, with figures of Our Lord and the apostles, and the Sacrifice of Isaac, probably carved in Antioch.

Lower part of the cases. A third-century sepulchral cist containing the burnt bones of a woman, found in 1866 near the Church of St. Ursula, Cologne. It originally contained the gilded glass disk, No. 628, in Table-Case B (fig. 91).

To right and left of the cist are reproductions of Early Christian objects and emblems from Great Britain. Some of the objects are in the Museum, e. g. the cakes of pewter with the sacred monogram found in the Thames at Battersea (cf. fig. 38), and a pewter dish from Appleshaw in Hants, on which the monogram is roughly incised (Room of Roman Britain, Wall-Case 47).

Wall-Cases 5 and 6.

Framed on the wall are ten cedar panels of the thirteenth century (p. 154) from a door in the Coptic Church of St. Mary (*Al-Mu' 'Allaka*), at Cairo, carved with Christian subjects alternating with scrolls of Saracenic design (No. 986). The subjects are the

Annunciation and Baptism (plate XIII), Nativity, Entry into Jerusalem, Descent into Hell, Pentecost and Ascension. On the right of the large frame is a Byzantine panel-picture probably of the thirteenth century, from a monastery near the Natron Lakes, north-west of Cairo: the four scenes are the Annunciation, Nativity, Baptism, and Transfiguration; the picture belongs to a period from which little work of the kind has survived. On the left of the frame is a Russian ikon of the Virgin and Child in an enamelled silver frame, both of comparatively modern date.

On the shelf are various objects of early date. The ivory liturgical diptych of the seventh century from Egypt, probably Hermonthis (Erment), belongs to a class noted above, and the lists of names and prayers written upon it are remarkably complete (p. 114, fig. 66). Two fifth-century blue glass vases from Amiens (Nos. 658-9), represent one of the earliest forms of chalice used in Early Christian times (p. 106 and fig. 64), and may have been themselves chalices. Among other glass vessels are a goblet (No. 652, of the fourth to sixth century) found at Cologne, engraved with Adam and Eve, Moses striking the Rock, and the Raising of Lazarus; a globular vessel of similar date, also from Cologne, with a Greek inscription, *Drink and live*, cut in relief round the sides; and a moulded bottle (fourth to sixth century) with a cross, palm-branch, and human figure from Syria (fig. 92). The large silver Byzantine chalice with a dedicatory inscription (sixth century) was also obtained in Syria (fig. 65, and p. 108). On the shelf are also two Visigothic bronze vessels from Spain, a ewer and basin of the sixth to seventh century (plate XII), with inscriptions recording the maker's name and a verse from the Bible (Rev. v. 5); and the glazed pottery bowl known as the Constantine bowl, with an incised figure of Our Lord and inscriptions relating to Constantine in the interior: doubts have been cast on the authenticity of this bowl on the ground of the close similarity of the incised design to a much later representation. At the back of the shelf are two circular marble disks from Palmyra in design resembling the stamps for eucharistic bread used in the Coptic Church. The Greek inscriptions round the edges are however different.

At the bottom of the cases are three wooden models of churches inlaid with pearl-shell, made in Palestine, two representing the Church of the Holy Sepulchre at Jerusalem, the other, the Church of the Nativity at Bethlehem.

Wall-Cases 7 and 8.

The top shelf of these cases is occupied by a series of bronze lamps and other bronze objects mainly from the Christian East. In the middle is a fifth- or sixth-century bronze seated figure of the literate type holding a book, and perhaps representing an apostle.

On the shelf, Case **7**, is a silver treasure found at the close of the nineteenth century near Kyrenia, on the north coast of Cyprus; and consisting of a plate, a shallow basin, a hexagonal censer, and a number of spoons. From considerations of style, and from comparison with other examples of Byzantine silver chiefly in Russian collections, this treasure, which probably belonged to a church or monastery, may be ascribed to the sixth century. Byzantine silver plate of this class is thought to have been extensively made in Syria, whence it was largely exported; the Russian examples were traded into the interior of that country in exchange for furs, and have been principally found in the Government of Perm, together with contemporary silver dishes of Persian (Sassanian) workmanship. The large plate with the nielloed cross in the centre (No. 397, plate IX) is an almost exact parallel to a plate in the Hermitage Museum in Petrograd. The saint represented in relief in the centre of the basin (No. 398, plate IX) is St. Sergius or St. Bacchus, one of two popular Syrian martyrs, who were captains of the foreign division of the Imperial Body-guard, and are identified by the peculiar collar worn round their necks as a sign of their military rank. The censer (No. 399, fig. 68), which once had a bronze lining, is of an early form, replaced in later times by a bowl-shaped type with a high foot: on three of its faces are Our Lord between St. Peter and St. Paul; on the opposite three faces are the Virgin between St. John and St. James (?). The spoons, which were perhaps originally private property bequeathed at the death of the owner to the Church, may have been used for entertaining guests or feeding the poor, such a use of silver spoons in early times having been recorded; many of them are remarkable for the animals depicted upon the bowls, recalling the similar animals seen upon mosaics and sculptures of the Early Byzantine period. One is punched with the name of a former owner, Theodore.

An interesting point in connexion with this treasure is the occurrence on the bottom of the censer and the large plate of a number of stamps of several 'hall-marks', many examples of which are known to exist on pieces of Byzantine silver (fig. 77). Similar stamps may be seen on objects belonging to the contemporary Lampsacus treasure, in Wall-Case **11**. The shelf of Case **8** contains part of the Esquiline treasure (see below).

At the bottom on the left are arranged small objects, chiefly bronze, including part of a collection from El Azam, near Siût (Asyût), Egypt; crosses, ornaments, toilet implements and disks. On the right are bronze stamps for marking property, some with owners' names, others with acclamations, dating from the fourth to the sixth century; among them is a bronze relief of a mounted saint (St. George?) from Akka, Palestine. In the centre are silver spoons of the fifth century found in 1886 in the neighbourhood of Rome and inscribed with names and monograms inlaid with niello.

Wall-Cases 9 and 10.

In these cases and on the lower shelf of Case **8** is exhibited the silver treasure, dating from the fourth to the fifth century, found in 1793 near the Church of SS. Silvester and Martin on the Esquiline Hill at Rome. It comprises the toilet articles of Projecta, a Roman lady of rank, wife of Secundus, a member of the great family of the Asterii, whose name, with that of her husband, is inscribed on the lid of the large casket (No. 304) on the shelf in Case **9**. The inscription, which is preceded by the sacred monogram ☧, runs: *Secunde et Projecta vivatis in Chri(sto)*, proving that its owners belonged to the Christian community. The figures on the body of the casket (plate VI), which was evidently a bridal gift, are Projecta and her attendant maids; round the lid is an interesting scene depicting the first entrance of the bride into her husband's house, mythological groups representing Venus, and nereids with tritons and sea-monsters; and on the top, portrait-busts of the married pair in a medallion of the style seen on sarcophagi of the same period (fig. 18). It may be remarked that the old custom of conducting the bride to her husband's house in a festal procession with dances and songs was continued by Christians, though the scene here represented is doubtless purely pagan in character. This casket, with its mythological subjects, has been quoted as an illustration of the laxity of Christian sentiment prevailing about the close of the fourth century. Other interesting parts of the treasure are the dome-shaped casket (No. 305) ornamented with figures of the Muses, and containing silver bottles for perfumes and essences similar in form to an example recently found at Traprain Law (p. 65); a large ewer (No. 307) bearing the inscription, *Pelegrina, utere felix* ('Pelegrina, may good luck attend thy use of me!'); an elegant flask with embossed ornament (No. 306); a large fluted dish (No. 310), also with affinities to the Traprain treasure; two sets of four circular and four rectangular dishes with inlaid monograms (Nos. 312–19); two ornaments (Nos. 336–7), probably from the arms of a chair, in the form of fore-arms holding pomegranates: four figures (No. 332) representing the personifications of Rome, Constantinople, Alexandria, and Antioch, perhaps serving to ornament the ends of the poles of a litter; silver-gilt horse-trappings (*phalerae*) (Nos. 338–43); and a number of smaller objects, brooches, pins, rings, and charms. The brooches (*fibulae*) include examples much older than the treasure as a whole, and going back to a time before the Christian era.

The miscellaneous nature of the objects comprising the Esquiline treasure suggests that the whole may have been buried at some time of danger, such as a barbaric invasion.

Wall-Cases 11 and 12.

The collection of bronze lamps and other bronze objects is continued on the top shelf of these cases. Attention may be drawn to the lamps in the form of birds (Nos. 509–13). In the middle is a steelyard weight (fig. 14) in the form of the head of an emperor, perhaps Phocas (A. D. 602–10). On the shelf, Case **11**, is exhibited a small silver treasure of the sixth century, found at Lampsacus on the Hellespont. It comprises a tripod lamp-stand (No. 376), beneath the foot of which are two impressions of an official 'hall-mark'; a cylindrical vessel with foot (No. 377), perhaps a chalice (p. 110), two circular shallow dishes (Nos. 378–9) with monograms, perhaps patens, one having beneath it more Byzantine official stamps (plate VIII); a border for a table(?) made of beaten silver; fragments of a folding-stool or stand made of silver with iron cores; fragments of a gold necklace and ear-ring; and an interesting series of spoons having monograms on the sides (fig. 77ª) and metrical Latin and Greek inscriptions on the handles and bowls, derived from the Eclogues of Virgil and the traditional sayings of the sages Solon, Bias, Chilon, and Pittacus. Four other spoons bear the names Mark, Luke, James, and Peter, perhaps in this case referring to Apostles, though as a rule the names found on spoons are those of their owners. All the inscriptions and monograms are or were inlaid with niello.

On the right, Case **12**, is a silver treasure of the later fourth century found on the Hill of St. Louis, Carthage (Nos. 356–75). It consists of two hemispherical dishes without Christian characteristics, but with pastoral and animal scenes, human masks in relief, and pearled edges: one has a figure-subject on a medallion at the bottom: these dishes show analogies with similar objects in the Traprain treasure (p. 65); two dishes, one having an inscription with the sacred monogram and a reference to the Cresconii, a well-known family in North Africa in the fourth and fifth centuries, another an inscription, *loquere feliciter* (speak under good omen), with the sacred monogram between *alpha* and *omega*; a shallow bowl with long handle, and in the centre in high relief a frog, sometimes regarded as a symbol of resurrection (cf. the lamps, p. 181); three low hemispherical bowls, one with a cover, in the centre of which is a high rim serving as a foot for the lid, which may have been used as a separate dish; six spoons with deep circular bowls and short handles, a panel between handle and bowl bearing in each case a nielloed cross between scrolls; two complete spoons and a fragment, with pear-shaped bowls, on the backs of which is leaf-ornament like that upon the spoons from Cyprus in Wall-Case **7**; and a spoon with a shallow circular bowl in which is engraved the sacred monogram (☧) between *alpha* and *omega*. Included in the treasure are personal ornaments; a gold necklace with a lion's head at each end, a necklace of pearls alternating with precious stones, a pair of ear-rings, a gold finger-ring; two intaglios with a head of the type of Hercules and a figure of Fortuna respectively, and an onyx cameo with the head of Minerva.

The bottom of the cases is occupied by a large capital from Memphis, with a channel on each side, perhaps to receive the ends of screens, presented by the British School of Archaeology in Egypt; a cast from a figure of the Good Shepherd incised on a marble slab in a catacomb at Sousse (Hadrumetum) in Tunis (third to fourth century): here the bearded type should be noted, as well as the lamb, which apparently belongs to the fat-tailed African species; a marble panel with bust in relief from Carthage; architectural fragments from the Wadi Sarga Collection (p. 177).

Wall-Case 13.

On the floor of this case is a richly-carved limestone Coptic tomb-stone (seventh to eighth century); in the upper part is a monogrammatic cross between columns, and an inscription in Greek commemorating a lady named Sophrone; in the lower part is a bird (dove or eagle) with a medallion round its neck and a cross in its beak (No. 942, and see fig. 101).

On the shelf is a Coptic medallion of limestone carved with a similar bird holding an olive-branch in its beak.

It should be noted that an interesting series of Coptic tombstones is to be seen in the Department of Egyptian and Assyrian Antiquities (Second Northern Gallery, Room V).

Wall-Cases 14 and 15.

On the main shelf are exhibited a number of tomb-stones (No. 931, etc.) from Carthage, Gaul, and Spain (fourth to sixth century). Two of them (Nos. 931 and 935) are from the graves of children, one eight years, the other three months old. The earthenware slabs (No. 932 and No. 934, fig. 3) with the sacred monogram and inscriptions should be noted. On the front part of the shelf are various carved fragments of limestone or marble. The marble fragment (No. 941), in the shape of two right hands holding a table engraved with the sacred monogram, is of interest, as having been probably broken from a sarcophagus sculptured with the *Traditio Legis*, the scene in which Our Lord gives the Law to St. Peter. On the top shelf and floor are tombstones with Coptic inscriptions (seventh to eleventh century) from the Wadi Sarga Collection (see p. 177), commemorating monks. On the floor is also a tombstone (eighth century) from Memphis with a Greek inscription: *In the name of the Father, the Son, and the Holy Ghost.*

SERIES OF OBJECTS FROM WADI SARGA,
NEAR SIÛT (ASYÛT), EGYPT.

(Mostly in Wall-Cases 11–23.)

This site was excavated by Mr. R. Campbell Thompson in the winter of 1913–14 for the Committee of the Byzantine Research and Publication Fund, by which the antiquities discovered were presented to the Museum. The place is about fifteen miles south of Siût (Asyût), and is situated in a cleft of the hills formed by an ancient watercourse. The walls of many ruined buildings still stand, built of unburned brick on stone foundations. In the limestone cliffs are large quarry-caves in which evidence of a pre-Christian occupation was found; but the chief feature of interest in the main cave was an apse with a mural painting representing the Communion of the Apostles. A painting on stucco from the ruins of a villa about two miles north of Wadi Sarga is exhibited in Wall-Cases **16** and **17**.

During the excavations various sections were cleared on the slopes where the houses had been built close together. In some houses were found capitals of limestone columns, fragments of pottery and glass, small objects of bronze, wood, clay, leather, and basket-work with fragments of woven tapestry of papyrus and a number of inscribed potsherds (*ostraka*), now transferred to the Department of Egyptian and Assyrian Antiquities. Limestone funerary tablets (Wall-Cases **14** and **15**) were fairly common, as were fragments of ornamental sculpture (Wall-Cases **16–19**).

The finds made at Wadi Sarga seem to show that the place was occupied by poor and industrious people; sections cut in the neighbouring cemetery yielded no objects of exceptional quality. The bronze coins discovered date mostly from the reigns of Justinian (A. D. 527–65) to Maurice Tiberius (A. D. 580–602); one is a Mohammedan coin of the Early Ummayad dynasty (about A. D. 670–750). The date suggested for most of the objects is thus the second half of the sixth century, a period with which the character of the antiquities is in accord.

Wall-Cases 16 and 17.

On the wall of the case is a mural painting taken from the ruins of the above-mentioned villa in the neighbourhood of Wadi Sarga. It represents the Three Children of Babylon in the burning, fiery furnace with the 'angel' behind them in the flames (fig. 70); the two great medical saints SS. Cosmas and Damian stand on each side, and their three brothers Anthimos, Leontios, and Euprepios below. First under the Three Children is a Coptic inscription which reads: *The threescore martyrs of Siût: their day the twelfth of Mekheir. Hourkene the little, my brother Mena the little—Jesus Christ.*

The Three Children appear to be by a different hand from that which executed the other figures, though probably not much earlier in date; the subject is on a separate square of plaster: round this a second artist seems to have painted the larger figures which were unfortunately damaged and are much restored. Perhaps all the work was executed within the limits of the sixth century.

On the slope are the coins mentioned on p. 177, and fragments of pottery with boldly painted human heads and animal figures. Two large fragments are painted with representations of combats of men and beasts in a Hellenistic style. On the bottom are architectural fragments with characteristic acanthus-ornament, and a limestone stand for water-bottles elaborately carved on the front (fig. 6).

Wall-Cases 18 and 19.

On the shelves are Coptic architectural fragments, mostly from Wadi Sarga. Particularly fine is the treatment of the formal leaf-design in the example shown in fig. 72; presented by the British School of Archaeology in Egypt; here the method of relieving the design against a background of deep shadow is well illustrated (cf. p. 127). Those illustrated in figs. 73 and 74 should also be noted, as also the portion of a frieze in the centre of the lower shelf (fig. 5), on which the series of pottery fragments with painted animal figures is continued. The pottery doll and small birds should also be noticed.

At the bottom of the case are further architectural fragments: two capitals, one from Wadi Sarga, another from Memphis, and fragments of tomb-stones with Coptic inscriptions.

On the wall at the back of the case are two water-colour sketches, from photographs and coloured tracings, representing the general appearance of the frescoed quarry-cave.

Wall-Cases 20 and 21.

On the shelves is a series of Coptic pottery vessels from Wadi Sarga. These include the large urns with painted linear and conventional ornament, vases, bowls, cups, jugs, plain or painted, with one or two handles. Attention may be drawn to the broken vase with two human masks in relief on the neck (fig. 22).

On the wall of the case are several photographs of Wadi Sarga, one showing the cave with mural paintings.

At the bottom are a limestone capital and the base of a column from Wadi Sarga, and a fine marble foliated capital of early date from Harâm-esh-Sherîf, Jerusalem.

Wall-Case 22.

On the top shelf are various fragments of two-handled pottery vases (*amphorae*) painted with letters and marks. On the slope is a series of pottery fragments from Wadi Sarga with painted geometrical and conventional designs; above these are two dishes of red earthenware from Memphis, each with a Cross in the centre; a framed fragment of an amphora, with a military saint painted in outline, from Oxyrhynchus (Behnesa), Egypt; some miscellaneous objects from the Wadi Sarga Collection, including a bronze lamp and a bronze lid of scallop form.

In the bottom of the case are different sculptured architectural fragments, the base of a column from Wadi Sarga, and clay seals for wine-jars with monograms.

Wall-Cases 23 and 24.

On the top shelf are various architectural fragments: pilaster-capitals from Wadi Sarga; two portions of cornices from Shurifat; two fragments carved with foliage, a lion, bird, and human head from Medinet el-Fayûm (figs. 7 and 8); a stucco female head, a piece of moulding, and a floriated capital from Memphis, given by the British School of Archaeology in Egypt.

On the slope are exhibited a selection of pottery lamps and pilgrims' flasks (*ampullae*). The lamps fall into two main groups: one, chiefly from Carthage, Sicily, and Italy, represented almost entirely by the type shown in fig. 20; the other, comprising more varied forms, obtained in Egypt, Syria, Palestine, and Asia Minor. The greater part of these lamps date from about the sixth century, and their forms differ from the older Roman types, examples of which may be seen among the Romano-British Collections in the Room of Roman Britain. Lamps of this kind were used for ordinary domestic purposes, but were also deposited in or near the tombs of the dead and kept burning at shrines of martyrs. The majority of those in the collection were obtained from excavations at Carthage, which was a great centre of their manufacture; these are mostly made of a rather bright red ware, distinct from the buff-coloured pottery which usually characterizes the lamps of Egypt, Syria, and Palestine, while the designs upon them are more finely executed. On the other hand, the majority of lamps with inscriptions come from the latter countries. See examples at the bottom; and in the Sixth Egyptian Room on the lower shelves of Wall-Cases **273–9**.

Attention may be specially drawn to the following lamps: No. 718 (fig. 20), Jonah and the monster; No. 720, Daniel with an angel and Habakkuk; No. 721, Our Lord trampling upon the dragon; No. 727, the Spies with the grapes of Eshcol; to the various animals represented in Nos. 728 to 753, among which the dove occurs most frequently; to the various forms of the sacred monogram, Nos. 758 to 781; and to the crosses on the succeeding numbers: and to the mould (No. 804), with intaglio designs, for the upper half of a lamp (top row of slope, Case **24**): the top and bottom halves of these lamps were made separately, and stuck together before being placed in the furnace.

The terracotta flasks (*ampullae*) were connected with the shrines of saints or other holy places. It was the custom of pilgrims, especially about the sixth century, to carry away flasks of this kind filled with the oil used for the lamps kept burning before the shrines of Saints and Martyrs; the most famous examples, which were made of lead, are those sent from the Holy Land to Theodolinda, Queen of the Lombards, in the early seventh century, and still preserved at Monza in Italy. The majority of the terracotta *ampullae* come from Egypt and bear representations of St. Menas or Mennas, an Egyptian martyr of the military or official class, decapitated during the persecutions of Diocletian's time. The legend relates that the saint's body was placed upon a camel which was let loose to follow what course it chose; and that in the place where the camel stopped, some miles from Alexandria, a grave was made and a shrine subsequently built. In allusion to this legend, St. Menas is constantly represented as standing between two camels (fig. 51), though the animals are often of so fantastic a form as to be very difficult to recognize. This subject is commonly found on one side of the flasks, the other side generally having a Greek inscription meaning 'the blessing of St. Menas'. In many examples, e. g. Nos. 886–92, a head of negroid appearance is seen, possibly representing a Libyan. The martyrdom of St. Menas is represented on the ivory box in Wall-Cases **3** and **4** (No. 297, plate IV).

At the bottom of the cases are two Jewish ossuaries or repositories for the bones of the dead, of the Roman period, from Palestine, and a number of lamps, mostly from Egypt, which could not be accommodated on the slope. These ossuaries were made to contain the bones from *loculi* in Jewish catacombs when, in process of time, space became scarce and the *loculi* were required for fresh interments. The ornament commonly found upon them, 'rosettes,' concentric circles, arcading, etc., includes both oriental and Hellenistic elements such as we might expect to find in a country with no individual art of its own and receptive of various artistic influences from abroad. Other ossuaries are shown at the bottom of the next two Wall-Cases.

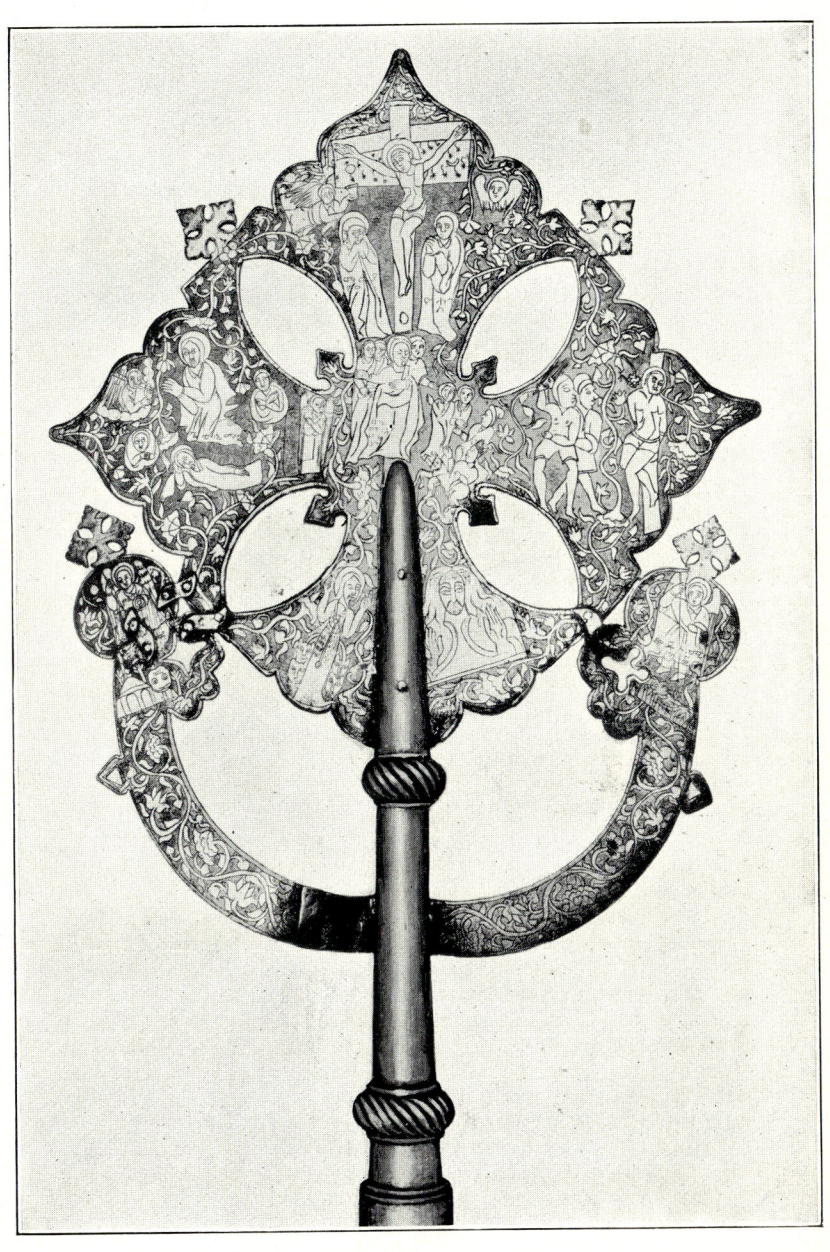

PLATE XV. GILT BRONZE CROSS FROM ABYSSINIA.
(*See* p. 181.)

Wall-Case 25.

On the wall of the case is a linen grave-tunic from Egypt, possibly from Akhmîm (Panopolis) with tapestry ornament in the form of stripes and medallions (*clavi, orbiculi*); among the designs may be recognized the Virgin and Child, and, in the larger medallions, the Adoration of the Magi (fig. 99). On the shelf are framed tapestry fragments from El Azam, between which is a fragment of the sixth century, probably from Akhmîm, with a woven design representing a mounted figure, and the word *Zacharias* in Greek characters, perhaps the name of the weaver who produced it in Alexandria (fig. 100). A few fragments of tapestry from Wadi Sarga are also exhibited.

On the bottom of the case is an ossuary of the type mentioned above, from Jerusalem, with a series of pottery lamps of the fourth to the sixth century from Ehnasya, Egypt, illustrating the degradation of a design composed of a frog (cf. p. 175) and two ears of corn. There are also a few *ampullae* which could not be accommodated in Wall-Cases **23** and **24**.

Attention may be drawn to the ossuary with incised designs in the bottom of the adjoining Wall-Case (**26**). It was found in a burial cave on the Mount of Olives, on land belonging to John Gray Hill, Esq., by whom it was presented. It bears at the top of one end incised inscriptions in Greek and Hebrew, stating that it contained the bones of Nikanor 'who made the gates'. This Nikanor is mentioned both in the Talmud and by Josephus, and the gates were those in the Temple of Herod called by his name. The character of the inscriptions points to an early date in our era.

Wall-Cases 26-30.

Upper Part, including the shelves.

Objects relating to the Abyssinian Church (cf. p. 114). The thick wooden altar-tablets are used to support the model tabernacle called *tâbut*, supposed to copy the Ark of the Covenant brought from Jerusalem by Menelek I, son of Solomon and the Queen of Sheba; the example in the middle of the shelf, Case **26**, should be noted. In Cases **27-8** is a silk altar-cloth with woven figures; and Cases **27-30** contain an interesting series of brass processional crosses, among which attention may be called to the fine example in Cases **27-8**, engraved with religious subjects (plate XV). Other objects worthy of notice are the silver chalices and paten and a silver chalice (fig. 103): bronze and silver censers; two silver ornaments from tops of ceremonial umbrellas, one with a painted medallion of St. Michael; a manuscript upon skin (p. 156) in Ge'ez, the liturgical language of Ethiopia; objects used in the religious dances which form an important part of Abyssinian services, notably the priests' rattles (*sistra*) shaken to accompany the dancers. On the wall of Case **26** is a modern religious painting in vivid colours with the Virgin and Child, angels, and a mounted saint transfixing a dragon. The bronze patera (No. 534, fig. 12) is stated to have come from Nubia.

Bottom of the Cases.

Case **26** contains the inscribed ossuary noticed above (p. 181). In Cases **27** and **28** are various objects almost entirely from Egypt: fragments of flat pottery dishes of red ware impressed with Christian designs; a pottery lamp with inscription 'O God, the Father Almighty', and an ostrakon bearing a Greek receipt for taxes dated A.D. 135 found with it on the island of Elephantine, near Assuan, by Field-Marshal Earl Kitchener; other pottery lamps which should be studied in connexion with those in Cases **23** and **24**; plaster seals (Nos. 958–68) from wine-jars with religious subjects, the sacred monogram, or inscriptions (fourth to seventh century); inscribed pottery tiles; limestone stamps; crutch used by Abyssinian priests as a support during long services or for beating time in religious dances (cf. fig. 102).

The lower part of Cases **29** and **30** is mostly occupied by small objects from Egypt: bone panels carved with floral designs and human figures, in the Hellenistic style of Alexandria; pectoral cross and two pendants, each with a rudely carved figure of St. George and the Dragon; two carved wooden panels, one with an inscription; two wooden stamps (Nos. 981, 982); a wooden comb with Arabic inscriptions found at Akhmîm; two circular cakes with Greek inscriptions used in the Coptic Church (p. 69); ivory fragments, possibly parts of a casket, with incised and painted ornament; a pair of Coptic gilt leather slippers, a pair of sandals, etc.

On the south wall of the gallery above Cases **17** and **18** is a large Abyssinian religious picture upon canvas with the Crucifixion, obtained by Mr. J. Theodore Bent in 1893 and presented by him to the Museum. Like the engravings upon the metal crosses, it shows traces of Western (Portuguese) influence in the treatment of the central subject; for instance, the feet of Our Lord are pierced with a single nail, whereas in Eastern Crucifixions and in the West up to the thirteenth century, the feet are nailed separately. The picture was found cast on one side, because the colours were somewhat faded, in the Church of the Saviour of the World at Adowa; but it cannot be of any great antiquity, as many of the accessories of costume and equipment are similar to those in use in Abyssinia at the present day. Round the principal subject are grouped smaller scenes representing events in the history of Our Lord; among these are the Flagellation and Entry into Jerusalem.

Table-Case A.

The east side of the case is devoted to small objects, mostly of bronze, and money-weights of bronze and glass (see p. 138). Attention may be specially drawn to the intaglio plaque No. 543, representing a figure, possibly an emperor, riding into a town (sixth century); to the Byzantine bronze-gilt plaque of St. Theodore (No. 544, fig. 27); bronze relic-crosses (*c.* twelfth century), chiefly found in Egypt and Asia Minor (Nos. 558 ff.), the example, No. 559, fig. 16, being specially worthy of notice. Nos. 425-84 are *exagia* or standard money-weights (p. 138), with their denominations usually inlaid in silver on the upper surface. Many of the examples, which chiefly date from the fifth and sixth centuries, have on them the names of prefects and officials controlling the standards of weights and measures, as is the case with Nos. 433, 435, and 436. Occasionally imperial busts occur, and on No. 444 is the name of Theodoric, showing that these weights were used in the Gothic dominions of Northern Italy. Sometimes the surfaces have inlaid busts, and in the pound-weight (No. 483, fig. 89) two military saints are represented. The adjoining small circular glass money-weights (Nos. 660-85) are of the same period. They are usually stamped on one side with a bust or monogram accompanied by the name of an Eparch, or provincial governor; the majority come from Egypt and Syria.

Among other objects in the case should be noted the lead flasks or *ampullae*, the most interesting of which is the example (sixth to seventh century), from El Azam, Egypt (fig. 15), probably made in the Holy Land and brought home by an early pilgrim. On one side are the Maries at the Tomb, on the other is the Incredulity of St. Thomas : such *ampullae* are believed to reproduce as far as possible subjects depicted in the memorial churches at the Holy Places (p. 30).

On the west side are engraved gems, cameos, carvings in precious stones, rings, *fibulae* (brooches), etc.[1]

The earlier gems with symbolic subjects in the style of the period of the Catacombs are in the upper rows, and comprise examples of the Good Shepherd, the anchor with doves and dolphins, the palm-branch, the dove, the ship or galley, and the sacred monogram. Nos. 25 (*526*) (fig. 85) and 26 (*527*) deserve especial attention on account of their size, and because they are engraved with composite subjects, each combining the Good Shepherd with the History of Jonah. Attention may be also drawn to Nos. 11-16 (*512, 513, 1, 2, 514, 515*) which are engraved with acclamations, Nos. 12 and 14 bearing also the names of the recipients,

---

[1] Where two catalogue-numbers are quoted, the first refers to the *Catalogue of Early Christian Antiquities*, the second, in italics, to the *Catalogue of Engraved Gems*.

Deusdedit (God-given) and *Rogatus*; to No. 10 (*511*) which represents a triangle, perhaps symbolic of the Trinity; to No. 43 (*544*) (fig. 55), which is a very early example of the Crucifixion (see p. 88); and to No. 48 (*540*) (fig. 28) not later than the fourth century, which has a fish engraved in intaglio upon the emerald of its bezel.

Below the gems of earlier type are arranged others of rather later date, including three (Nos. 93–5) with early Byzantine monograms of about the sixth century, and a sapphire (No. 96) with a cruciform Byzantine monogram of similar date, perhaps representing the name Thomas. There are also a few cameos of Byzantine workmanship; No. 105, *7*, of about the eleventh century, represents St. John the Baptist; another (No. 104, *6*, fig. 86) has a very exceptional treatment of the Annunciation, the Archangel Gabriel being represented in the form of a winged genius in the classical style. Next to these are several larger cameos, or rather carvings, in heliotrope, jasper, and steatite, some of them, such as the bust of Our Lord (No. 106, *8*, fig. 87), considered to date from the eleventh or twelfth century, others being probably later.

Among the collection of rings without gems are a number of Early Christian and Byzantine examples of bronze, silver, and gold. No. 49 (fig. 30) is a remarkable ring, perhaps of the fourth century, with an openwork inscription, *Accipe dulcis multis annis* 'Accept (this present), sweet one, (and may it be yours) for many a year!' showing that it was once a gift and perhaps a betrothal ring. No. 50 has engraved on it in Latin, *Arborius, mayst thou live in Christ!* with the sacred monogram between Alpha and Omega; and the next few rings and bezels of rings, some of which are engraved with portraits in intaglio, are inscribed with acclamations of a similar character. No. 60 has a monogram with a cross, and No. 77 the later form of the sacred monogram (☧) in openwork. The lower rows contain Byzantine rings, some of which, like Nos. 190 (fig. 82) and 207 (fig. 31), are of very fine workmanship and go back perhaps as far as the fifth century, while others like Nos. 120, 168, and 189 (fig. 83) are only a century or so later. Nos. 171, 177, and 178 have typical cruciform monograms (cf. fig. 96), and No. 143 has the Greek inscription common on Byzantine rings: *O Lord, preserve the wearer*. No. 129 (fig. 32) is a fine example of a well-known class of Byzantine gold and nielloed marriage-rings of about the tenth century, to which the succeeding numbers also belong. Upon the bezel may be seen Our Lord blessing the bridegroom and the Virgin blessing the bride, while below, in Greek, is the word *Concord*; on the sides of the octagonal hoop are represented scenes from the history of Our Lord. No. 121 has on the bezel the Annunciation with 'Hail, thou art highly favoured' (St. Luke i. 28). On the bezel of No. 130 Our Lord stands between the bride and bridegroom with His hands upon their shoulders, the inscription being *Concord*, as before; round the hoop is a further Greek inscription, part of St. John xiv. 27, 'My peace I give unto you'. Nos. 131 and 132 have almost identical subjects. No. 133 differs in having only the busts of Our Lord and the bride and bridegroom upon the bezel. The silver ring, No. 142 (fig. 84), has a Medusa-like face upon the bezel, with seven radiating serpents, showing that it was worn as an amulet for protection against disease or accident, the design being commonly employed for this purpose. Round the hoop is the inscription noticed above: *Lord, preserve the wearer*, which also occurs upon the adjoining numbers (fig. 84). The gold rings, Nos. 171 (fig. 96) and 172, afford a good example of the commonest form of Byzantine monogram, the letters of the name being distributed on the extremities of a cross. This type of monogram is especially frequent between the eighth and tenth centuries. The large gold ring, No. 210, the hoop of which is moulded to represent two hares, has for bezel a coin of the Emperor Marcian (A.D. 450-7), and can thus almost certainly be assigned to the fifth century. No. 211 belongs to the sixth century, the coin which forms the bezel bearing the effigy of Justinian.

The gilt bronze buckle and belt-plates with classical figures in relief (Nos. 258-61) may date from the third or fourth century. They were found on the site of the Tombs of the Prophets at Jerusalem with the *fibula* (No. 257) bearing a cross, which is perhaps of the late fifth century, and the rock-crystal spindle-whorls (No. 262 and 263), which resemble similar objects found in Early Teutonic graves in northern Europe.

Table-case B.

The eastern half of the case contains the collection of gilded glasses. Nos. 608-10, 612, and 613 show portraits of husbands and wives with names and acclamations, No. 608 being pagan in character with a figure of Hercules in the centre, No. 613 having in the same position a small figure of Our Lord holding a wreath over the two heads (see above, p. 135); No. 610 (plate X) includes a little girl named **Lea** who stands between her parents, the field being occupied by the sacred monogram, a wreath, and the inscription. No. 615 is an example of a Jewish subject, showing the seven-branched candlestick, the ram's horn (*shofar*), the citron (*ethrog*), and bundle of branches (*lulab*), all objects used at Jewish feasts; and No. 619 (plate XI) represents Daniel destroying the dragon of Bel with the cake, as related in the Apocryphal History of Bel and the Dragon, verse 27. Nos. 630 (plate X) and 631 are examples of the youthful and ideal portraits of Christ characteristic of the first centuries of Christian Art (see

p. 86); No. 636 represents St. Peter and St. Paul, in this case both alike, and not showing the usual differences mentioned on p. 87; No. 605 is a portrait of an official or scribe holding a scroll, and with a case of *styli* for writing near his head; and No. 603 (plate XI) shows us a gladiator (*retiarius*) named Stratonicus, with his trident in his hand, and an inflated skin for practising boxing in the background. The box with a glass top contains the remarkable flat glass disk No. 628 (fig. 91), covered with designs etched in gold foil, and heightened by colour, found in 1866 in Cologne in a cist containing the burned bones of a woman (see Wall-Cases **3** and **4**). Though it probably had a protecting glass, the designs have suffered much from exposure and attrition. The surface is divided into eight compartments with Biblical subjects. Reading from the top round to the left, these are: two scenes from the Story of Jonah, Daniel in the lions' den, the Three Children of Babylon in the fiery furnace, the Healing of the young man born blind, the Widow of Nain, the Healing of the paralytic and the Dream of Ezekiel. In the centre was probably the Good Shepherd; remains of an inscription round this scene include the word *Dulcis*, and it was probably an acclamation to a departed soul.

Other Early Christian glass, not gilded, includes a fragment of a bowl with part of the motto *drink and live* in Greek characters; a fish of blown glass, No. 654; and a fragment from a cup, No. 655, with a fish in relief. The six large bone rings, No. 988, are from the Catacombs, and are said to have been impressed in the mortar of the *loculi*, like the gilded glasses. Above the disk are the fragments of a bowl of transparent glass (No. 629), also found at Cologne, studded with small blue and green medallions with Scriptural subjects. Among these may be mentioned Adam and Eve, the sacrifice of Isaac, the Three Children in the fiery furnace, the Story of Jonah, and Daniel with the lions. Beneath are a number of medallions once forming part of a similar bowl. Of the subjects which they represent will be found: Jonah and the Monster, Daniel, Lazarus in his tomb, and Our Lord carrying the rod or wand which is assigned to him in Early Christian Art as the emblem of miraculous power. The case also contains a number of fragments, one or two modern attempts at the reproduction of gilded glass in the old style, and two medallions, one representing a boy, the date of which is uncertain.

In the western half of the case are jewellery and other ornaments with reproductions of coins. The coins reproduced, which range from the reign of Constantine I (about A. D. 314), to that of Valens (about A. D. 368), illustrate the cross, sacred monogram, and the *labarum* (p. 79); the original of the medallion of the Emperor Justinian, now lost, was formerly in the Bibliothèque Nationale at Paris. The jewellery includes a necklace, ear-rings, and a pierced disk (fig. 78), from a large chain covering breast and back (sixth century) found in Egypt (probably at Antinoë) and given by Mrs. Burns; a bracelet of the same period (No. 279, fig. 81) with pierced designs and a bust of the Virgin on the clasp, from Egypt or Syria; gold buckle-plates with imperial busts in niello, found with coins of Constantius in Asia Minor, and dating from the fourth century (Nos. 253-4), a small reliquary of the tenth century, with a nielloed representation of the Nativity on the front, a cross with monogram on the back and an inscription showing that the contents were relics of SS. Cosmas and Damian (No. 284); two gold pectoral crosses, one (No. 285, fig. 79) with an inscription (Galatians vi. 14), the other (No. 287, fig. 80) with nielloed figures of Our Lord, the Virgin in the attitude of prayer between two angels, and a military saint (St. Theodore or St. George) transfixing a dragon with a spear; a cross-bow shaped *fibula* (No. 264), perhaps of the fifth century, with a Greek inscription: *The Grace of God*; various gold ear-rings, including examples of the lunate type, also found in barbaric graves in Hungary (sixth to seventh century); and a later jewelled and enamelled pectoral cross (eleventh to twelfth century). The ear-rings (No. 267) may be specially remarked for their early cloisonné enamel-work, in the form of birds and rosettes.

Objects outside the Cases.

In the north-east corner (above Wall-Cases **4** and **5**) is a Coptic limestone capital of the sixth century from Tell esh-Shurafa near Heluan, Egypt; in the south-east corner (above Cases **12** and **13**) is part of a slab of grey stone carved with a cross in relief within a circle; in the south-west corner is the capital of an engaged column carved with two figures; in the north-west corner is a grey stone cornice with arcading and a cross in high relief.

Standing on the floor in the south-west corner is a marble slab carved on both sides in oriental style (p. 127, fig. 75) with animal and other designs, including the double-headed eagle and the fountain of living water surmounted by the pine cone. It is said to have come from a church at Miafarqin, north-east of Diyarbekr, and dates from the period between the tenth and thirteenth centuries.

Objects in other parts of the Museum.

Iron Age Gallery (adjoining). The Franks Casket (p. 67) is exhibited in a special case between the Table-Cases. Enamelled brooches (cf. p. 145) and the Anglo-Saxon royal rings (p. 68) are in Table-Case **D**. The so-called 'pillow-stones' from Hartlepool carved with crosses (p. 67) are on the shelf in Wall-Cases **34-5**. The silver chalice from Trewhiddle, Cornwall, is in Wall-Case **52**, the stoup from Long Wittenham (p. 68) in Wall-Case **38**, the gold cross with coin of Heraclius in Table-Case **D,** and the Ostrogothic enamelled brooch in Wall-Case **61**.

Room of Roman Britain. The Roman pewter service from Appleshaw, Hants (p. 66), is exhibited in Wall-Case **47**. The metal ingots from Battersea stamped with the Sacred Monogram are seen in Table-Case **A**.

Department of Egyptian and Assyrian Antiquities. Room V, Second Northern Gallery, contains an important collection of Coptic antiquities, including a number of sculptured tombstones and capitals.

In the Fifth Egyptian Room are Coptic textiles (Table-Cases **G** and **H**) and Gnostic gems (Table-Case **I**).

King Edward VII Gallery. The ivory carvings (described above, pp. 169, 170) are exhibited in Bay xx, Table-Case and Pier-Case **A**, **B**, and **C**.

North-west Staircase. On the walls are several pavement mosaics found at Carthage, of which some are Christian. No. 7 (probably fifth century) is covered with semicircles rising from chalice-like vessels, with peacocks and other birds in the field and in one part a hart and a hind drinking from a fountain of four streams with the word FONTES (streams); another (fig. 49) has also harts drinking from a vase; crosses are seen in other parts of these mosaics.

Mausoleum Basement (Department of Greek and Roman Antiquities). A late-Roman sarcophagus (No. 2320, fig. 52) has on the front a representation of the marriage-feast of Cupid and Psyche. The subject was one of those adopted in Christian art, and the general restraint of the treatment, with various iconographical details, such as the fish on the table in front of the couch, and the peacock, emblem of immortality, have led some authorities to regard the sarcophagus as Early Christian.

Department of Manuscripts. Byzantine illuminated manuscripts belonging to this Department are exhibited in the Grenville Library, Cases **1** and **8**. The latter case contains the twelfth-century Psalter of Melisenda, wife of Fulk, Count of Anjou and King of Jerusalem, with fine carved ivory covers of the same date (Nos. 28, 29, *Catalogue of Ivory Carvings*).

INDEX

Abraxas (Abrasax), 162.
Abuna, 154.
Abyssinia, 6, 98, 154–7, 181, 182.
Adiabene, 4.
Africa, 12, 13.
Alpha and Omega, 80.
Altar-cloth, Abyssinian, 181.
Altar-tablets, Abyssinian, 114, 181.
Ambon (ambo), 100.
Amida (Diyarbekr), 4.
Ampullae, 179, 180, 183.
Anchor, 77.
Anchorites, 6, 26.
Anglo-Saxon antiquities, 68.
Animals, symbolical, 78.
Ankh (crux ansata), 81.
Antioch, 4.
Appleshaw, pewter from, 66, 128, 171, 188.
Arab Conquests, 42, 43.
Arabia Felix, 6.
Archangel, diptych with, 169.
Architecture, 91–9.
Arcosolia, 72.
Arians, 159.
Armenia, 4.
— influence of, 42.
Armorica, *see* Brittany.
Art, influences on Christian :
    Late-Hellenistic, 17, 18.
    Syrian, 18–20.
    Persian, 20, 21.
Arts, 116–52.
Asia Minor, 6, 7.
Asterisk, 112.
Athos, Mount, 52, 55, 120, 167.
Augustine, St., 60.

Basilica, 91–4.
— interior of, 99, 100.
Battersea, pewter from, 66, 171, 188.
Belfries, 97.
Bells, 97, 98.
Bema (presbyterium), 100.
Bewcastle, cross at, 61, 66, 126.
Bracelets, 133.
Brancaster, ring from, 66.
Britain, Early Christianity in, 56–68.
Brittany, 11, 57, 58.
Brooches, 183, 185.
Bulgaria, 7.

Cameos, 136, 184.
Cancelli, 100.

Carthage, 12.
Carthage treasure, 175, 176.
Casket of Projecta, 174.
Cassiodorus, 34.
Casts of ivories, 169–71.
Catacombs, 69–76.
Cathedra, 100.
Cedar panels, Coptic, 154, 171, 172.
Cemeteries, 74.
Censers, 113, 167.
Chalices, 68, 106–10, 129, 172.
China, 6.
Christ, portrait of, 85, 86.
Churches, English, 61–4.
Churches, models of, 172.
Ciborium, 103.
Cist, sepulchral, 171.
Cloisonné :
    Enamels, 45, 144, 145, 187.
    Jewellery, 131, 145.
Coins, 137, 138, 178, 179.
Colatorium, 111.
Cologne, 10.
Constantine bowl, 172.
Consular diptychs, 170.
Coptic Churches, 98.
Copts, 31, 152–4.
Corbridge, silver vessel from, 65, 128.
Costume, 89–91.
Cotton Genesis, 122.
Cretan School, 121.
Cross, the, 80, 81.
Crosses :
    Pectoral, 131, 187.
    Processional, 114, 181.
    Relic-, 183.
    Russian enamelled, 167, 168.
Crown, penitential, 168.
Crowns, marriage-, 135.
Crucifixion, 88, 89.
Crutch, Abyssinian priest's, 155, 182.
Cupid and Psyché, 81, 82.
Cuthbert, St., coffin of, 67.
Cyprus treasure, 173.

Dates, list of, 163–6.
Dating, system of, 73.
Dextera Dei (Domini), 86.
Diakonikon, 97.
Diptych, ivory liturgical, 114, 172.
Diptychs :
    Consular, 170, 171.
    Ecclesiastical, 113, 114.

Disk, gilded glass, 110, 171, 186.
Dome, 94.
Dorsetshire, 65, 66.
Dove, 78.

Ear-rings, 132, 133, 187.
Ecclesiastical use, objects of, 106–16.
Edessa, 4, 30.
Egypt, 6, 31, 32, 152–4.
El Azam, 173, 181, 183.
Embroidery, 152.
Enamels, 45, 144–7.
Encaustic painting, 121.
Esquiline treasure, 127, 128, 174.
Ethiopian manuscript, 181.
Eutychians (Monophysites), 159, 160.
Evangelists, symbols of, 81.
Exagia, 138, 183.

Fan, liturgical, 111.
Fibulae, 183, 185.
Finger-rings, 133–5.
Fish ('Ιχθύς), 76.
Flabellum, 111.
Fondi d'oro, 140–3, 185, 186.
Franks Casket, 67, 68.
Fresco, 121.

Gandhara sculptures, 25.
Gaul, 10, 11, 36, 46.
Gems, engraved, 136, 183, 184.
Georgia, 4.
Germany, 12.
Glass, 139–44.
Glasses, gilded, 135, 140–3, 185, 186.
Glass vessels, 106, 144, 172.
Gnostic objects in England, 66, 162.
Gnosticism, 160–2.
Goldsmith's work, 130–6.
Gospel Covers, 113.
Gospels:
    Edgmiatsin, 122.
    Lindisfarne, 68, 122.
    of Rabula, 122.
    Rossano, 122.
Greek Church, 157, 158, 167, 168.
Greek-Cross churches, 95, 96.

Hadrumetum, 13, 76, 176.
Haikal, 104.
Hand-bells in churches, 98.
Hartlepool, 67.
Heresies, 159–62.

Iconoclasm, 40–2.
Iconography, 76–91.
Iconostasis, 102.
Ikons, 102, 167, 172.

Illuminated manuscripts, 122.
India, 6.
Indictions, 73.
Inscriptions, 72–5.
Intaglio gems, 134, 136.
Interiors of churches, 99 ff.
Ireland, Christianity in, 57–9, 60.
Italy, 9, 10.
Ivories and casts:
    in British Museum, 169, 170.
    in other collections, 170, 171.
Ivory carving, 125, 126.

Jacobites, 160.
Jewellery, 131 ff.
Justinian, medallion of, 186.

Labarum, 79.
Lamp-holders, 102, 167.
Lamps:
    Bronze, 167, 175.
    Pottery, 179, 180.
Lampsacus treasure, 175.
Lance, Holy, 112.
Liber Pontificalis, 111.
Lindisfarne, 59.
Lindisfarne Gospels, 67, 68.
Liturgical diptych, 114, 172.
Lombards, 43, 45.
Long Wittenham, stoup from, 68, 187.

Mandorla, 84.
Manzikert, 49.
Marriage-crowns, 135.
Marriage-rings, 134, 135.
Maximianus, chair of, 125.
Melchites, 160.
Melisenda, Psalter of, 52, 188.
Mesopotamia, 4.
Moesia, 7.
Monasticism, 6, 26, 34, 35, 51.
Money-weights, 138, 183.
Monogram, the sacred, 79, 80.
Monophysites (Eutychians), 159, 160.
Monothelites, 160.
Monte Cassino, 34, 51.
Mosaics, 78, 121.
Mural paintings, 104, 105.
—from Wadi Sarga, 117, 177, 178.

Narthex, 92, 100.
Nestorians, 159.
Nimbus, 82, 83.
Nisibis, 4.
Northumbria, 59, 66.
Nubia, 6.

INDEX

Orans, 81.
Orpheus, 81.
Ossuaries, 180-2.
Ostraka, 177, 182.

Painting, 116-23.
Paintings, Abyssinian, 182.
Paintings, mural, 104-6.
Pala d'Oro, 145.
Palestine, 2, 4, 30.
Palm-branch, 78.
Panel-picture, 173.
Panels, carved cedar, 154, 171, 172.
Pantokrator, 105.
Patens, 110, 111, 129.
Patera, bronze, 182.
Pebble, inscribed, 168.
Périgueux, 97.
Persia, 4, 15, 20, 24, 32, 43.
Pewter, stamped, 66, 128, 171, 188.
Pilgrims' flasks, 179, 180, 183.
Pillow-stones, 67, 187.
Polycandela, 102, 167.
Pottery, 147, 178-182.
Presbyterium (bema), 100.
Projecta, casket of, 174.
Prothesis, 97.
Pyx, forms of, 112.
Pyxides, casts of, 169, 170.

Rattles, Abyssinian priests', 114, 156, 182.
Ravenna, 28, 97, 117, 125.
Reculver, 62, 63.
Rings, Anglo-Saxon royal, 68, 187.
Rings, finger-, 133-5.
Romano-British antiquities, 61-6.
Rome, 9, 10, 28, 36, 43-5.
Russia, 8, 9, 52.
Russian enamelled crosses, 167, 168.
Ruthwell, cross at, 61, 66, 126.

Saints, representations of, 87, 88.
SS. Cosmas and Damian, 117, 177, 187.
St. Mark's, Venice, 51, 95, 97.
St. Menas, 169, 180.
St. Peter's, Rome, 93.
SS. Sergius and Bacchus, 173.
Sarcophagi, 74.
Scandinavia, 12.
Scotland, 56-7, 59, 61, 65.
Sculpture, 123-7.
Seals, 137.
Seleucia, 4.
Serbs, 7, 53.
Shepherd, the Good, 77, 78.
Ship, 77.

Sicily, 52.
Silchester, 56, 61, 65, 66.
Silk, 149-152.
Silk-worm, 150.
Silversmith's work, 127-130.
Simantron, 97.
Spain, 11, 12, 37, 47.
Spoon, eucharistic, 111.
Spoons:
  Inscribed, 174, 175.
  Ornamented, 173.
Stag, 78.
Stamps:
  Bronze, 173.
  Limestone, 182.
  on Byzantine silver, 129.
Steelyard-weight, 175.
Strainer (*colatorium*), 111.
Subsellia, 100.
Swastika, 81.
Symbols, 76-84.
Syncretism, 17.
Syria, 4, 18, 23, 28, 117.

Tapestry, Coptic, 149, 181.
Tempera, 121.
Textiles, 147-52, 168, 181.
Thames, stamped pewter from, 66, 171, 188.
Thrace, 7.
Tiles, 182.
Tombstones, 74, 75, 176.
Traprain silver treasure, 65, 111, 128, 174, 175.
Trèves, 10.
Trewhiddle, chalice from, 68, 108, 187.
Triangle, 79.
Tunics, fragments of Coptic, 168.

Ulfilas, 8, 9.

Vaults, 94.
Venice, 51.
Vestments, 115, 116.
Victoria and Albert Museum, 47, 122, 149.
Vine, 79.
Virgin, portrait of, 86, 87.
Visigothic bronze vessels, 172.
Visigoths, 36, 37, 38, 47.

Wadi Sarga, 177.
— Mural painting from, 117, 177, 178.
— Objects from, 176-9.
Wine-jar seals, 182.